Easy Diabetic Diet After 50

2100 Days of Delicious, Low-Sugar & Low-Carb Recipes. A Practical Guide for Prediabetes & Type 2 Diabetes, including a 60-Day Meal Plan for a Healthy Lifestyle

Sophie Wood

Table of Contents

INTRODUCTION

Diabetes is a chronic health condition. Millions of people around the world are affected by this condition. To inform you about diabetes, we have created a cookbook for all health-conscious and diabetic individuals, especially those over 50, who want to know more about managing their blood sugar levels. This cookbook will contain all the invaluable information you need to maintain a balanced and healthy diet while keeping your blood sugar levels in check.

What is Diabetes?

Diabetes refers to high blood sugar levels. It is a metabolic disorder that means the body fails to produce sufficient insulin or cannot use it properly. The pancreas is responsible for producing insulin. It is a hormone that directs glucose absorption from the bloodstream to the body's cells to turn it into energy. When the cells in the body fail to do so, glucose accumulation occurs, leading to hypoglycemia.

Diabetes has three main types:

- Type 1
- Type 2
- Gestational Diabetes

Type 1 diabetes is an autoimmune condition where the immune system disrupts insulin production by accidentally attacking the cells in the pancreas. Individuals with Type 1 diabetes need to take insulin injections every day to survive. Moreover, it is a disorder mainly diagnosed in childhood or early adulthood. It has nothing to do with changing your diet or lifestyle.

Type 2 diabetes, on the other hand, can be managed through good dietary habits. It is a common condition that can occur later in life due to an unhealthy diet, poor lifestyle habits, genetics, and obesity. With an active lifestyle and the right, balanced diet, type 2 diabetes is reversible.

Gestational diabetes can occur during pregnancy and usually subsides after childbirth. However, people with this type of diabetes do run the risk of developing type 2 diabetes later.

Careful management and regular check-ups are crucial to managing diabetes and preventing future risks. Moreover, you need proper knowledge of this condition to get a good start. It is why we have created this Diabetic Cookbook After 50.

Our recipes blend balance with healthy nutrients, low-glycemic ingredients, and proper portion sizes to keep your blood sugar levels in check and encourage optimal health. This cookbook is your resource for a fulfilling lifestyle. Not only does this cookbook provide you with all the knowledge to keep diabetes under control, but it also includes delicious recipes that offer a great way to treat your taste buds and make informed food choices.

It is also a valuable source for people concerned about their loved ones suffering from diabetes and wishing to help them actively. We aim to promote well-being and find a solution to manage diabetes easily and in an inspiring way.

Read on further for deeper insights into diabetic dietary habits, following an active lifestyle, and creating a perfect meal plan to get started.

The Importance of a Balanced Diet

A balanced diet plays a vital role in controlling blood sugar levels. It includes an appropriate portion of carbohydrates, proteins, and fats while not neglecting essential vitamins, minerals, and fiber for a nutrient-rich diet that covers all aspects of a healthy and balanced diet.

Being a diabetes patient means being extra mindful of your diet, as every food choice impacts your overall health. A well-rounded diet allows you to keep your blood sugar levels regular and improves your lifestyle, reducing complications and preventing serious health issues in the future.

Benefits Of a Balanced Diet

Blood Sugar Control

A diet with all the crucial nutrients and vitamins can help you maintain stable blood sugar levels by reducing the likelihood of surges after meals. Stable glucose levels also lower the risks of further complications, such as developing neuropathy or retinopathy afterward.

Weight Management

One of the main risk factors linked to type 2 diabetes is weight gain, in other words, obesity. A diet focusing on nutrients while keeping calories on the lower side helps in weight fluctuations or loss.

Cardiovascular Health

Diabetes may lead to potential heart health issues. A diet balanced with fiber and free from unhealthy fats can lower the risks of such a severe condition.

Consistent Energy Levels

With blood sugar levels that are constantly fluctuating, your energy levels experience a surge and drop, too. But with a balanced diet that curbs the spikes, your energy levels will likely stay consistent throughout the day.

Managing Diabetes with A Balanced Diet

A balanced diet helps to cancel out potential medical conditions associated with suffering from diabetes, such as hypertension, heart disease, cholesterol, and excess weight gain.

So, it's a diet consisting of complex carbohydrates like whole grains, legumes, and vegetables. These food choices keep your energy levels up throughout the day and allow glucose to flow gradually into your bloodstream, slowing down the risk of sudden spikes.

Moreover, the inclusion of lean proteins and healthy fats in diabetic meals helps you to stay sustained for longer without the need for binge eating or snacking, lowering the temptation to munch on unhealthy snacks.

Especially if you're in your 50s, weight management is crucial with diabetes. It can give way to further complications. It's best to start with a balanced diet and get on with managing this disorder.

Understand Your Diet

As we have already established, diabetic people have specific dietary needs. It would help if you were wary of the components of a diabetic diet, such as exchanging simple carbs for complex carbohydrates, adding fiber-rich foods and lean proteins, and substituting trans fats or saturated fats with healthy fats in your meals.

Portion Control

Consuming appropriate portion sizes can help control calorie and carb intake, essential for maintaining stable blood sugar. You can use small-sized plates, bowls, or even measuring tools to handle portion sizes for each meal. Also, you can introduce colorful vegetables to your diet for more fulfilling meals without the fear of too many calories.

Meal Planning

Planning beforehand can save you a lot of time and money. Plus, it combats the need to indulge in unhealthy eating choices. Create a meal plan with all the essential nutrients for diabetic patients and one that fits into your eating schedule. Either plan a weekly or monthly menu and include a balanced mix of whole grains, fresh fruits, lean proteins, legumes, vegetables, and low-fat or plant-based dairy products.

Meal Prep

Giving a few hours to meal prepping and cooking in advance can save time and energy for later on. For example, cooking large meals and stocking them in containers to set yourself up for the week ahead can save you a lot of effort and unnecessary decision-making. In better words, you'd always have something healthy to look forward to, even in a time crunch, without having to resort to unhealthy food choices.

Make A Grocery List

Write down a grocery list before heading to the supermarket. A detailed list of ingredients for your meal plan will help you stick to what you need and avoid buying unnecessary items. Always choose fresh, whole foods over processed foods.

Choosing Variety

A balanced diet for diabetic individuals does not have to be boring. You can add a variety of colorful vegetables and experiment with a bunch of different ingredients and flavors while testing other cooking techniques. By experimenting, you can enjoy fulfilling meals and tastes without getting tired of monotonous foods.

A diabetic and balanced meal plan is necessary to maintain blood sugar and promote overall well-being. So, exert creativity in your meals and enjoy the excitement of cooking to stay healthy and happy.

Tips for Adopting Healthy Eating Habits

Maintaining blood sugar levels and overall health, especially after 50, requires the right approach to diabetes. Learning the right strategies and setting realistic goals can help you move forward with managing life as a diabetic person. A motivated mindset and a positive outlook are the most critical steps of this diet. Nothing will work If you're unwilling to make efforts for your health.

Set smart goals and track your progress to ensure you are doing what you need to do for flexibility and adaptability. Remember, living as a person with diabetes and making the best of what you can will help you immensely in the long run. It's a whole lifestyle change, and if you're up for it, following the steps below will set you up on the correct path.

Consult With a Professional

Of course, as a person with diabetes, you're bound to find out in one way or the other. Before you commit to any goals, talk with a healthcare professional like a registered dietitian or endocrinologist. They can offer personalized advice by keeping your preferences, medical history, and current blood levels in mind. Moreover, they may provide you with a meal chart and plan as a clear roadmap of what to follow and avoid.

Monitor Your Blood Sugar Levels

It's essential to monitor your blood sugar levels regularly before deciding on setting some realistic goals. Be mindful of any fluctuations or patterns in your sugar levels. Doing so would help you focus on committing to goals based on your needs.

Set Achievable Goals

Small goals are the way to go. You cannot change your lifestyle in a fortnight, and nobody asks you to. Instead, set small, achievable goals you can complete every day. For instance, you can reduce carbohydrate intake by 10 grams daily or take a 15-minute walk after dinner to get used to an active lifestyle. Small, baby steps can allow you to familiarize yourself with living life as a diabetic person, and you will start to see significant improvements over time.

Take on bigger goals once you are motivated and encouraged to do more. Starting with smaller steps gives the confidence of achievement. You can utilize that feeling for bigger, more beneficial goals once ready. Big goals could include:

- Introducing more physical activity to your routine.

- Adding low-glycemic foods.

- Lowering your blood sugar levels to a certain percentage.

Bigger goals are more demanding but with more rewards in return.

Celebrate Achievements

If you're not patting yourself on the back for coming so far, who will then? Celebrating your milestones by rewarding yourself after completing each commitment would be best. Celebrating your journey and achievements is crucial for building motivation and staying strong in your progress. You can start with a small indulgence of your favorite food, buy something you always wanted to tick off your wish list for a long time, or share your celebrations with your loved ones.

Adapt to the Changes

Controlling blood sugar levels is not determined by a single universal solution. It takes trial and error to adjust to a routine you like. You must stay flexible and adapt to the changes throughout. Your goals need to be customized occasionally, and you should be ready to adjust accordingly, whether through lifestyle, medical, or health-based choices. Be positive and more accepting of your situation and view it to improve yourself, not get distressed.

Make note that changing your lifestyle for diabetic control is a process, not a hurdle. It takes time to get used to these changes. Take your time, start small, and be consistent. And you will never know when these adjustments will become a part of your routine and a regular part of your life.

Meal Planning Tips & Stocking Pantry

To support nutrition, you must ensure each meal has a good mix of carbohydrates, proteins, and fats for a more fulfilling, blood sugar-regulating experience.

Similarly, stocking your pantry with these helpful, nutritious ingredients would ensure you have a working pantry ready for creating delicious, diabetes-centered meals.

Whole Grains

They should be the main priority! Go for a range of whole grains such as oats, brown rice, quinoa, whole-grain bread, and whole-wheat pasta. Whole grains include complex carbohydrates which keep you sustained for the long haul. They also provide essential fiber, which prevents spikes in blood sugar by slowing down glucose absorption into the bloodstream.

Healthy Oils

Pick heart-healthy choices such as olive, avocado, and coconut oil. Such oils have monosaturated fats and are abundant in antioxidants, which help promote a healthy heart and manage blood sugar levels conveniently. You can use these oils in dressings, roasting, and sautéing.

Legumes

You need to add a variety of canned and dried legumes to your stock. You can choose lentils, chickpeas, and black beans. You can include these varieties in soups, salads, stews, and even as a primary ingredient for homemade dips. They are a fantastic source of plant-based protein, fiber, and minerals.

Nuts & Seeds

Some excellent additions to a diabetic pantry are walnuts, almonds, cashews, chia seeds, and flaxseeds; they are your best friends. They are great to snack on and can be used as a garnish for salads, oatmeal, and yogurt bowls or added to baked goods. They are a great source of protein, fiber, and healthy fats.

Low-Sodium Broths

Keep a steady stream of low-sodium vegetable or chicken broths in your pantry. They make for an excellent base for cooking soups, stews, and sauces, adding their unique flavor and consistency to each dish without excessive sodium that can do more harm than good, especially for elderly diabetic people. You can make broths too with fish and chicken. These add well-needed lean protein into your diet, keep you sated for a long time, and improve muscle health.

Herbs & Spices

You don't always need to rely on salt to add flavor to your dishes. Instead, it would be best if you stocked up on various herbs and spices that can be better than salt. Some of them are oregano, cayenne pepper, turmeric, and cinnamon, which can add depth and an exciting taste to your meals.

Sugar Substitutes

Since the priority is to control blood sugar levels, be wary of traditional white sugar. Choose natural sweeteners like date syrup, monk fruit extract or juice, Stevia, erythritol, and raw fruits. These substitutes fulfill your sugar cravings without causing a jump in blood sugar levels. Moreover, you can use them for baking and sweetening beverages.

A well-stocked pantry will set you up for success. You'll have the gateway for experimenting, and with so many ingredients in hand, you'll likely get more creative with planning and cooking healthy meals.

Grocery Shopping for Diabetes

You need to start making wise choices in food to beat diabetes, especially in your 50s. First, start with making a detailed list of items you need. It will keep you on track, and you'll be more willing to skip things you don't need, no matter how tempting.

Food Labels

The primary step to being smart with grocery shopping is getting the hang of food labels. Choose low-sugar, low-fat, and low-sodium options. Look closely at serving sizes, as consuming more than you need is always risky. Make high-fiber, whole grain, and lean proteins the priority, and ignore sugary drinks, unhealthy fats, and processed foods.

Fresh Produce

Fresh fruits and vegetables are your best companions. Make the produce section the highlight of your shopping. Add veggies and fruits full of essential minerals, fiber, and vitamins. Pay attention to filling your cart with low glycemic index (GI) food options like leafy greens, cruciferous vegetables, and berries. These picks have a low impact on blood sugar.

Lean Proteins

Choose lean proteins such as poultry without skin, tofu, and legumes. They are rich in nutrients and don't add cholesterol or unhealthy fats to your diet. Ignore processed meats as they are full of harmful additives and sodium.

Whole Grains & Fiber

Quinoa, brown rice, oats, whole wheat pasta, and brown bread are whole-grain options you need to add to your cart. They are rich in fiber and regulate blood sugar levels well. Similarly, pay attention to nuts and beans as they support a good blood sugar level and overall digestive health.

Essential Items for Diabetes

Even with all the essentials at hand, cooking delicious meals for a diabetic diet is a challenging task. However, with the right tools and kitchen essentials, you can make the process much easier and more intelligent!

Blood Glucose Meter

It is entirely unrelated to kitchen tools but a worthwhile purchase. It's an essential device for regularly checking blood sugar levels. It'll help you make knowledgeable decisions for your diet and encourage you to prioritize your health every day.

Food Scale

Portion control is a vital part of a diabetic diet. You need a food scale to accurately measure your portions for carbohydrate intake for managing blood sugar levels. Also, you can measure ingredients precisely with the food scale.

Nonstick Cookware

Such cookware eliminates the need for extra cooking oil or butter, which is excellent for avoiding excessive fats. Moreover, you get the advantage of enjoying healthier meals without compromising on taste.

Measuring Tools

When it comes to accurate portioning, measuring cups and spoons prove to be great lifesavers. You can measure your ingredients with them, particularly liquid and dry goods.

Spiralizer

You can create noodles with a spiralizer using vegetables like zucchini or sweet potato. It's a handy tool for your kitchen, especially for a diabetic person. Vegetable noodles make for a great low-carb substitute for pasta, so you can enjoy delectable foods without fearing a spike in your blood sugar level.

Blender

Any kitchen without a blender is incomplete. It stands for its versatility because you can make protein shakes and smoothies in it. You can make nutritious soups and sauces with a blender. It is helpful for quickly adding more fruits and vegetables to your diet.

Steamer Basket

Steaming your foods helps to preserve their nutrients and natural taste. A steamer basket is an excellent way to cook vegetables, fish, and other food items easily while maintaining a low glycemic index profile.

Slow Cooker

If you are a busy person with diabetes, a slow cooker can be an excellent kitchen investment. It lets you cook various flavorful dishes and preserves their nutrient profile. Slow cooking the foods break down complex carbohydrates slowly, which can be beneficial in managing blood sugar levels.

With a kitchen equipped with all these tools, you'll quickly know how to cook for diabetes. With accurate measurements, correct portion sizes, and all the versatile tools to cook at your disposal, you can make nourishing dishes that will not only feed your taste buds but will also keep you sustained for the long run!

Understanding Prediabetes and Type 2 Diabetes

Prediabetes refers to blood sugar levels that are higher than usual but not high enough to be diagnosed as type 2 diabetes. This condition is an alert sign for making lifestyle changes to stop the likelihood of developing diabetes later in life.

People with blood sugar issues or health-conscious folks should pay attention to prediabetes. You must keep a check on your blood sugar levels and follow a healthy diet and lifestyle in advance to put a stop to its progression.

Understanding diabetes and the pattern linking type 2 diabetes and prediabetes is the first step in managing future risks effectively. Learn about your health through a health practitioner. Start embracing a healthier lifestyle and making informed choices to stay free from diabetes later in life or to manage it in time.

The Role of Carbohydrates and Sugars in Diabetic Diets

Managing diabetes is all a matter of learning how different foods cause a spike in blood sugar levels. It is important to understand the role of carbohydrates and sugars in effectively controlling diabetes.

Carbohydrates:

They are a macronutrient that has a key impact on blood sugar surges. They break down into glucose and increase your blood sugar levels.

There are two types of carbohydrates: complex carbohydrates and simple carbohydrates.

Whole grain foods contain complex carbohydrates like legumes, vegetables, whole grains, and specific fruits. These foods are also high in fiber, which allows slow digestion, gradually absorbing glucose into the bloodstream. A slow release of glucose helps prevent sudden spikes in our blood sugar patterns.

Examples of simple carbohydrates are sugary snacks, candies, pastries, and sugary drinks. They get digested into our system quickly and raise blood sugar levels immediately.

Keeping an eye on carbohydrate intake is as important as monitoring blood sugar levels for diabetic patients daily. Consistent carbohydrate intake throughout every meal will stabilize your glucose levels and prevent sudden hunger pangs.

Sugars:

Sugars are simple carbohydrates! They might provide you with energy quickly but can raise your blood sugar levels rapidly, too, particularly in diabetic people.

It's crucial to understand the differences between natural sugars and artificial sugars:

Natural sugars are present naturally in fruits, vegetables, and dairy products. They may still affect blood sugar, but they accompany essential nutrients like fiber, vitamins, and minerals that balance out everything.

Added sugars refer to sugar present in processed foods or added in foods artificially. They bulk up extra calories without providing any nutritional value whatsoever. Desserts, sodas, snacks, and processed foods are some examples of added sugars that are not safe for consumption, especially for people with diabetes.

Diabetic patients should pay attention to foods with naturally occurring sugars, like fruits and dry fruits, which also offer extra nutritional benefits.

Being careful with carbohydrate and sugar intake is vital for efficiently managing glucose levels. Pay attention to these strategies to pave the way for a healthier lifestyle.

Weight Management and Diabetic Diet

Weight management is a crucial part of diabetes management. A diet based on portion control, caloric control, meal planning, balanced macronutrients, and an active lifestyle can help prevent high glucose levels and manage diabetes effectively.

There is no doubt that living with diabetes can be challenging, especially after 50. It's a condition that requires strategic planning and consistency, which may seem quite overwhelming at times. Plus, giving up is not an option or may lead to future complications.

To overcome obstacles and to learn to resist temptations in the beginning or whenever you feel you're losing motivation to continue: First, know that you're not alone.

Connect with others or fellow diabetic people, join support groups, follow like-minded individuals or online communities vocal about this condition, and show ways to improve your diet and health. Seek help from a healthcare professional to learn about diabetic care.

Sharing your thoughts and experiences with others will encourage you to remain steadfast in your health journey. It's natural to feel this way, but connecting with others and talking about your feelings can give you a sense of belonging and new ideas to manage this disorder.

Feel free to do this with others. Your friends and family can be part of your journey and be there for you whenever you need love and support. Educate your loved ones about diabetes and ask them to join you in living a healthy life. Create a support system for maintaining a balanced diet.

Tips For Eating Out

If you're dining out, carry out some research on the restaurant's menu. Search for foods that are diabetic-friendly and check the nutritional information if available. Doing your research beforehand will help you make informed choices on the spot.

Check Portion Sizes

Many restaurants provide large servings. Instead, try sharing the meal with your partner or have half of the meal packed to take home and eat later. You can also select an appetizer or light menu option that is more convenient for diabetes.

Go For Healthy Carbohydrates

Choose whole grains or whole wheat rather than refined options. Whole grains contain:

- A low glycemic index.
- They digest more slowly than refined grains.
- Prevent a sudden rise in blood sugar and keep you nourished for an extended period.

Slow Eating

Take your time eating and savor your food—no need to rush, and enjoy mindful eating. Slowly eating food can help with digestion and give your body time to alert you when your stomach is full.

Avoid Sugary Drinks

Please avoid sodas and fruit juices; they increase your blood levels immediately. Instead, go for sparkling water with a lime slice or unsweetened tea.

Be aware of the sauce.

Various sauces, dips, and dressings can contain excessive and unhealthy fats. It's best to have them on the side as you can adjust your eating amount.

Go For a Walk

What's best other than to go for a walk after a meal? It will not only refresh you but will also help regulate blood sugar levels and aid in digestion.

Tips For Socializing

If you receive a dinner invitation, you need to tell the host beforehand about your condition so they can personalize the menu for you ahead.

It would be best to consider only food options that fit your diabetic meal plan. Plus, keep glucose tablets and healthy snacks at hand to avoid sudden changes in your blood sugar levels. Similarly, keep monitoring and consider insulin or any medication before attending the event.

Keep a positive mindset and a friendly attitude, as added stress can be harmful and hurt your condition. Talk to your friends and families; they may offer you the advice and support you need.

Avoid overindulging in alcohol, as it can raise your blood sugar levels significantly. Either drink moderately or choose low-sugar concentrated drinks, such as dry wine spirits with sugar-free mixers. Or alternate with an unsweetened lemonade, sparkling water, or plain water if available.

Embrace the diabetic lifestyle to work on yourself. Diabetic cuisine can be a great help in nourishing your overall health. It will help keep blood sugar levels normal and teach you to cook and experiment with different foods, ingredients, and flavors. More than as a step to improve diabetes, take it as a lesson you can share with other diabetic individuals in your life.

When you feel too spent or discouraged by making continuous efforts, take a moment to slow down and breathe. You can always rest and start again tomorrow.

Exercises and Physical Activity to Complement the Diet

To overcome diabetes issues, including physical activities and staying active in your daily routine is essential. Regular exercise helps maintain blood sugar levels and can positively affect overall health.

Do Exercises You Enjoy

Do more physical activities you enjoy, such as walking, swimming, running, jogging, bicycling, dancing, or even practicing yoga. Staying active not only has benefits for your health but also lifts your mood and spirits.

Start But Small

Take baby steps If you are a newbie at working out or have been inactive for some time. Start small with doable activities and take a 10-minute walk around the block. Do easy stretching exercises or basic yoga at home. It will help you slowly build your strength towards more physically severe activities.

Socialize & Exercise

Working out is more fun when you have company. Either involve your family and friends with daily exercising activities like walks or bike rides. Or start going to the gym for exercise to meet other like-minded individuals and make friends with health goals.

Be Consistent Than Intense

The key to controlling diabetes is to stay consistent with physical activity rather than taking up intense workouts you can't stick to for long. Cutting down to shorter exercise sessions is much better than long stretches of physical activity.

Vary Your Exercise Routine

Instead of following a boring, cookie-cutter exercise routine, mix it up with various exercises and physical activities to prevent monotony and add fun to your workout routine. Include a combination of strength training, cardiovascular exercises, and flexibility workouts. A mixed routine can allow your body to get all your muscles working up, and you will be more willing to try varied exercises every day.

Monitor Your Blood Sugar Levels

Check the progress of your blood sugar levels every day, before, during, and after exercise. It will show how your diabetic levels react to different activities and help you plan your workout routine accordingly. It's wise to consult your healthcare practitioner and follow their advice on creating a safe and practical exercise routine for your specific condition.

Leading an active lifestyle and incorporating exercise into daily life ensures stable blood sugar levels. Physical activity is a form of building muscle strength and helps with digestion and overall well-being. Every action you take today will set you up for success later; everything you do now counts, and if you feel left out in your journey, grab a friend and let them be a supportive part of your journey for more enlivening and exciting life. Remember, two heads are better than one, and you can always back each other up when one of you feels demotivated and needs to buckle up.

Chapter 1:
Stable Blood Sugar Breakfasts

Yummy Jelly & Peanut Butter Oatmeal

Preparation Time: 2 minutes
Cooking Time: 5 minutes
Servings: 1
Ingredients:

- ½ cup gluten-free oats
- 1 mashed banana
- 1 tablespoon peanut butter
- 1 tablespoon raspberry jelly
- ½ teaspoon ground cinnamon
- ½ cup with 1 tablespoon of unsweetened vanilla almond milk
- 1-s tablespoon ground flax seed

Directions:

1. Add oats, ½ cup almond milk, cinnamon, and mashed banana in a small-sized saucepan.
2. Turn the heat on medium flame and stir for 3-5 minutes.
3. Within a few minutes, the oats will thicken, and the milk will evaporate.
4. After evaporating, add 1 tablespoon of almond milk.
5. Stir until the almond milk has also evaporated.
6. Transfer the oats to a bowl after taking them off the stove.
7. Serve with peanut butter and jelly.

Nutrition:
Calories: 354
Protein: 10 g
Fiber: 9 g
Carbohydrates: 49 g
Sugar: 10 g
Sodium: 134 mg
Fat: 16 g

Gluten-Free Banana Oat Muffins

Preparation Time: 5 minutes
Cooking Time: 19 minutes
Servings: 10
Ingredients:

- 1 pasture-raised egg or apple sauce
- ½ cup maple syrup
- 2 cup gluten-free oats
- 4 tablespoons melted coconut oil
- 1 ½ teaspoons cinnamon
- 1 teaspoon vanilla essence
- 1 teaspoon baking soda
- ½ teaspoon nutmeg
- 4 mashed bananas
- ¼ teaspoon salt

Directions:

1. Preheat oven to 350°F and transfer oats to a blender, grinder, or food processor.
2. Grind until oats form a flour consistency.
3. Add thoroughly mashed bananas, coconut oil, vanilla essence, egg, and maple syrup in a separate bowl.
4. Mix all together with a fork.
5. Using a spatula, put powdered oats, nutmeg, salt, cinnamon, and baking soda.
6. Combine all the fluid and dry ingredients properly.
7. Line the muffin tray with cupcake liners or grease them with oil.
8. Pour the batter into the liners and bake for 16-19 minutes.
9. Insert a toothpick; consider the muffins done if it comes out clean.
10. Let them cool, and serve them after.

Nutrition:
Calories: 138
Protein: 2 g
Fiber: 2 g
Carbohydrates: 22 g
Sugar: 13 g
Sodium: 105 mg
Fat: 6 g

Breakfast Chia Seeds Chocolate Pudding

Preparation Time: 10 minutes

Cooking time: 0 minutes

Servings: 2

Ingredients:

- 2 medium-sized ripe & mashed bananas
- ½ cup chia seeds
- 1 tablespoon maple syrup
- ½ teaspoon vanilla essence
- 2 cups unsweetened almond milk or coconut milk
- 4 tablespoons raw cacao powder
- ½ teaspoon cinnamon

Directions:

1. Combine the dry ingredients in a large bowl and whisk.
2. Add mashed banana, maple syrup, almond milk, and vanilla extract to the dry ingredients.
3. Using a whisk, mix everything well together.
4. Cover the bowl and leave it in the fridge for 2 hours. Or better, leave overnight.
5. This will thicken up the breakfast pudding.
6. Once the pudding has thickened, blend it until smooth.
7. Serve with nuts or eat as it is.

Nutrition:

Calories: 172

Protein: 4.7 g

Fiber: 7.8 g Carbohydrates: 22.1 g

Sugar: 9.2 g

Sodium: 91 mg

Fat: 7.8 g

Nutritional Tofu Scramble

Preparation Time: 5 minutes

Cooking Time: 10 minutes

Servings: 2

Ingredients:

- 2 tablespoons plant-based milk
- 1 tablespoon extra-virgin olive oil
- ¼ teaspoon garlic powder
- ¼ teaspoon turmeric
- 2 tablespoons nutritional yeast
- 1 16-ounce firm tofu block
- ½ teaspoon salt or as needed

Directions:

1. Set the pan over medium heat and heat olive oil.
2. Mash the chunk of tofu in the pan using a potato masher or your hands.
3. Stir tofu occasionally until the water has evaporated.
4. Add the dry ingredients to the pan, stirring for at least 5 minutes.
5. Stir the plant-based milk into the pan.
6. Serve hot with green vegetables if you like.

Nutrition:

Calories: 288

Protein: 24 g

Fiber: 4 g

Carbohydrates: 9 g

Sugar: 1 g

Sodium: 600mg

Fat: 18 g

Delicious Quinoa & Apple Breakfast Porridge

Preparation Time: 5 minutes
Cooking Time: 20 minutes
Servings: 2

Ingredients:

- 1 cup any unsweetened plant-based milk
- ¼ teaspoon cinnamon
- 1 teaspoon vanilla essence
- ⅛ teaspoon cardamom
- 1 chopped large apple
- ½ cup dry quinoa
- 1 tablespoon coconut oil
- 2 tablespoons unsweetened raisins
- A pinch of sea salt

Directions:

1. Rinse the quinoa well in a sieve to remove debris and "saponins," the outer layer contributing to bitterness.
2. Combine rinsed quinoa with milk, cinnamon, cardamom, vanilla extract, raisins, and sea salt in a saucepan. Incorporate well.
3. Bring milk in the saucepan to a boil over high heat.
4. Reduce the heat and cover the pan once it boils.
5. Simmer for 15 minutes or until all liquid is absorbed.
6. Let the steam sit with the lid for a few minutes after turning off the heat.
7. Heat coconut oil over medium heat in a separate pan while the quinoa cooks.
8. Transfer the apple chunks to the coconut oil and sprinkle the cinnamon.
9. Mix well and allow to simmer for approximately 10 minutes, until lightly browned and tender.
10. Mix the apple mixture occasionally so that they're evenly brown.
11. Top quinoa with sautéed apples and serve in bowls.
12. You may add any additional toppings you like or extra milk.

Nutrition:
Calories: 485
Protein: 9 g
Fiber: 7 g
Carbohydrates: 42 g
Sugar: 10 g
Sodium: 168mg
Fat: 33 g

Simple Avocado Toast

Preparation Time: 2 minutes
Cooking Time: 5 minutes
Servings: 2

Ingredients:

- 1 slice whole grain bread
- ¼ medium avocado
- 1 pinch of sea salt
- 2 teaspoons bagel seasoning (you can make your own as well)

Directions:

1. Toast the slice of bread in a toaster.
2. Mash the avocado and spread it on the toast.
3. Sprinkle it with the seasoning and sea salt.
4. Serve with the plant-based milk of your choice.

Nutrition:
Calories: 172
Protein: .5.4 g
Fiber: 5.9 g
Carbohydrates: 17.8 g
Sugar: 2.3 g
Sodium: 251mg
Fat: 9 g

Nut Cream Cheese & Strawberry Sandwich

Preparation Time: 10 minutes

Cooking Time: 0 minutes

Servings: 2

Ingredients:

- 2 cups sliced strawberries
- 8 oz. low-fat cream cheese
- 4 slices whole wheat bread
- 1 tablespoon Stevia
- 1 teaspoon grated lemon zest

Directions:

1. Cut the bread into halves and toast them in a toaster.
2. Add cream cheese, strawberries, Stevia, and lemon zest in a blender.
3. Pulse into a spreadable texture.
4. Spread the mixture on the bread to make a sandwich.
5. Serve and enjoy immediately.

Nutrition:

Calories: 123

Protein: .4 g

Fiber: 3 g

Carbohydrates: 19 g

Sugar: 5g

Sodium: 201mg

Fat: 4 g

Overnight Cinnamon Oats

Preparation Time: 5 minutes

Cooking Time: 0 minutes

Servings: 5

Ingredients:

- 8 teaspoons light brown sugar
- 2 ½ cups gluten-free oats
- 2 ½ unsweetened plant-based milk
- 2 ½ teaspoons vanilla extract
- ½ teaspoon sea salt
- 1 ¼ teaspoons ground cinnamon

Directions:

1. Assemble everything in a large bowl.
2. Give a mix and divide among 5 jars or as you like.
3. Cover with lids and refrigerate overnight.
4. Enjoy it for breakfast the next day.

Nutrition:

Calories: 197

Protein: 5 g

Fiber: 4 g

Carbohydrates: 34 g

Sugar: 7g

Sodium: 317mg

Fat: 4 g

Mango & Pomegranate Breakfast Smoothie

Preparation Time: 10 minutes
Cooking Time: 0 minutes
Servings: 2

Ingredients:

- ½ peeled grapefruit
- ¼ ground ginger
- A handful of baby spinach
- 1 cup frozen mango
- ⅓ cup pomegranate cherry juice
- 1 cup frozen red raspberries
- ½ cup plant-based milk
- ½ cup frozen banana

Directions:

1. Add mango, banana, milk, spinach, and ginger to a blender.
2. Blend to a puree and set aside.
3. Add raspberries, pomegranate, cherry juice, and grapefruit to a blender.
4. Blend until it forms a puree.
5. Add the two purees in layers into two cups to create a red and green effect.
6. Chill and serve!

Nutrition:

Calories: 310
Protein: .9 g
Fiber: 17 g
Carbohydrates: 63 g
Sugar: 33 g
Sodium: 70mg
Fat: 9 g

Breakfast Fruity Quinoa Mix

Preparation Time: 10 minutes
Cooking Time: 20 minutes
Servings: 4

Ingredients:

- 2 cups water
- 1 cup red quinoa
- 2 tablespoons coconut sugar
- 2 tablespoons chopped mint
- 1 ½ cups sliced strawberries
- 1 ½ cups chopped mangoes
- 1 ½ cups blueberries
- 1 lemon juice

Directions:

1. Add water to a pan and bring it to a boil over medium-high heat.
2. Mix in quinoa and cook for 20 minutes.
3. Transfer quinoa to a bowl, fluff with a fork, and garnish with fruits and lemon juice.
4. Serve immediately and enjoy your breakfast.

Nutrition:

Calories: 161
Protein: 5 g
Fiber: 17 g
Carbohydrates: 8 g
Sugar: 4 g
Sodium: 16mg
Fat: 2 g

Quick Breakfast Tacos

Preparation Time: 5 minutes
Cooking Time: 10 minutes
Servings: 2

Ingredients:

- ½ cup shredded low-fat cheese
- 16 oz. drained soft tofu
- ½ teaspoon garlic powder
- ½ teaspoon turmeric
- 3 tablespoons nutritional yeast
- ¼ teaspoon paprika
- 1 tablespoon low-fat butter
- Salt & pepper as needed
- Salsa
- 1 avocado
- Hot sauce
- 6 corn tortillas

Directions:

1. Set a large pan over medium heat and melt butter.
2. Add yeast, garlic, paprika, turmeric powder, and tofu.
3. Break the tofu into bite-sized pieces in the pan with a spatula.
4. Stir until the mixture is dry and sauté in cheese, salt, and pepper to taste.
5. Let it cook on low heat until the cheese has melted.
6. Add the filling to the tacos and serve immediately.

Nutrition:

Calories: 235
Protein: 19 g
Fiber: 2 g
Carbohydrates: 9 g
Sugar: 2 g
Sodium: 550mg

Fat: 9 g

Sweet Potatoes with A Twist

Preparation Time: 5 minutes
Cooking Time: 10 minutes
Servings: 2

Ingredients:

- 2 tablespoons low-fat yogurt
- 2 medium-sized sweet potatoes
- 2 tablespoons unsweetened almond butter
- 2 tablespoons maple syrup
- ½ cup homemade or store-bought Granola

Directions:

1. Clean the sweet potatoes thoroughly and poke holes with a fork.
2. Microwave them for 2 minutes, turn them over to the other side, and microwave again.
3. When done, it should be easy to pierce with a fork.
4. Let them cool.
5. Cut from the middle, ensure the insides face upward, and slightly mash the insides with a fork until a small mouth forms.
6. Fill it with almond butter, yogurt, maple syrup, and Granola.
7. Serve hot.

Nutrition:

Calories: 410
Protein: 9 g
Fiber: 8 g
Carbohydrates: 62 g
Sugar: 25 g
Sodium: 160mg
Fat: 16 g

Gluten-Free Blueberry Pancakes

Preparation Time: 5 minutes

Cooking Time: 10 minutes

Servings: 2

Ingredients:

- ½ cup frozen or fresh blueberries
- 1 cup gluten-free flour
- 1 teaspoon apple cider vinegar
- 1 cup sugar-free plant-based milk
- 3 tablespoons maple syrup
- 1 teaspoon vanilla essence
- 1 tablespoon baking powder
- ½ teaspoon salt
- 1 tablespoon coconut oil
- 1 tablespoon extra-virgin olive oil

Directions:

1. Pour milk and apple cider vinegar into a blender. Set aside for 3 minutes to make a substitute buttermilk.
2. Blend the buttermilk by adding maple syrup, olive oil, and vanilla essence until smooth.
3. Next, add in flour, baking powder, and salt. Beat everything until batter forms.
4. Place a pan or griddle over medium heat and melt coconut oil.
5. Check to see if the pan is hot. Place the batter on it to make 3-inch-thick pancakes, and keep a 1-inch distance between the pancakes.
6. As the pancakes are cooking, place blueberries on top of them.
7. Cook the pancakes from both sides for 3-5 minutes or until brown.
8. Serve hot with extra maple syrup.

Nutrition:

Calories: 565

Protein: 16 g

Fiber: 9 g

Carbohydrates: 87 g

Sugar: 5 g

Sodium: 262mg

Fat: 20 g

Crunchy Almond Cereal Breakfast

Preparation Time: 5

Cooking Time: 15

Servings: 8

Ingredients:

- 1 cup organic oats
- 1 cup organic spelt flakes
- ¼ cup date syrup
- 1 ½ cups roughly chopped almonds
- 7 tablespoons melted coconut oil
- Any plant-based milk

Directions:

1. Preheat your oven to 330 degrees Fahrenheit.
2. Line the baking tray with butter paper.
3. Add all the ingredients in a large bowl and mix it all together with a spatula.
4. The ingredients should stick together like granola bars.
5. Spread the mixture onto the baking tray.
6. Bake for 15 minutes or until they become crunchy.
7. Let it cool, and then break it into cereal-like pieces.
8. Serve with almond milk or any of your choice.

Nutrition:

Calories: 286

Protein: 6 g

Fiber: 4 g

Carbohydrates: 34 g

Sugar: 5 g

Sodium: 59mg

Fat: 14 g

Banana Cocoa Smoothie

Preparation Time: 10 minutes

Cooking Time: 0 minutes

Servings: 2

Ingredients:

- 3 cups plain and unsweetened low-fat yogurt
- ¼ unsweetened peanut butter or any nut butter
- 2 teaspoons unsweetened cocoa powder
- 3 frozen & sliced bananas
- 1 cup frozen cauliflower florets
- 2 teaspoons maple syrup

Directions:

1. Add all the ingredients to a blender or your favorite smoothie maker.
2. Blend everything until smooth
3. Serve in glasses with extra banana toppings.

Nutrition:

Calories: 583

Protein: 23 g

Fiber: 10 g

Carbohydrates: 79 g

Sugar: 18 g

Sodium: 210mg

Fat: 24 g

CHAPTER 2:
HEALTHY PASTA

Vegan Spinach Ricotta

Preparation Time: 15 minutes
Cooking Time: 50 minutes
Servings: 7

Ingredients:

- 20 oz frozen, thawed and drained spinach
- 4 cups low-sodium pasta sauce
- 3 cups low-fat ricotta
- 14 cannelloni tubes

Directions:

1. Turn the oven on to 350 degrees Fahrenheit.
2. Combine the spinach and ricotta.
3. In a baking dish, pour 2 cups of pasta sauce.
4. Fill cannelloni tubes with a piping bag filled with spinach and ricotta mixture.
5. Arrange the filled tubes in the baking dish and add the rest of the sauce.
6. Bake for 40 minutes, covered.
7. Remove the cover and bake for 5 to 10 minutes more.
8. Allow to cool for a few minutes before serving.

Nutrition:

Calories: 473
Protein: 16 g
Fiber: 6 g
Carbohydrates: 43 g
Sugar: 18 g
Sodium: 384mg
Fat: 28 g

Parsley Lemon Pasta

Preparation Time: 5 minutes
Cooking Time: 10 minutes
Servings: 3

Ingredients:

- 3 tablespoons extra-virgin olive oil
- 8 oz. long pasta
- ½ cup lemon juice
- 1 teaspoon lemon zest
- 3 minced garlic cloves
- ¼ teaspoon red chilli flakes
- Sea salt as needed
- ¼ cup chopped parsley
- Black pepper as needed

Directions:

1. As directed on the package, cook the pasta al dente.
2. Drain the pasta water and save half a cup of pasta water.
3. Run the pasta under cool running water before setting aside.
4. Heat oil in the pot in which you cooked the pasta.
5. Add the garlic and red pepper flakes and cook for about a minute.
6. Add the pasta and ¼ cup of pasta water, and heat until the pasta is warm.
7. Put the heat on low and add the lemon juice, zest, and parsley.
8. Stir and season with pepper and salt to taste.
9. Serve Immediately!

Nutrition:

Calories: 366
Protein: 10 g
Fiber: 3 g
Carbohydrates: 59 g
Sugar: 0.8 g
Sodium: 33mg
Fat: 9 g

Creamy Mushroom Stroganoff

Preparation time: 10 minutes

Cooking Time: 20 minutes

Servings: 4

Ingredients:

- 1 small finely diced yellow onion
- 3 minced garlic cloves
- 4 tablespoons extra-virgin olive oil
- 2 tablespoons whole-wheat flour
- 2 lbs. trimmed & sliced cremini mushrooms
- ¾ cup dry white wine
- ¾ low-fat sour cream
- 1 ¼ cup low-sodium vegetable stock
- 2 tablespoons chopped parsley
- Sea salt as needed
- Black pepper as needed
- 16 oz. whole-wheat pasta

Directions:

1. As directed on the package, cook the noodles until they are al dente. Drain and reserve ½ cup of pasta water.
2. Over medium-high heat, melt butter in a medium pot. Add onion and sauté for 5 minutes until golden.
3. Add garlic and mushrooms and cook for five minutes until the mushrooms become tender.
4. Stir in the flour for a minute, ensuring no white streaks.
5. Add the wine and vegetable stock on a medium flame and cook for 5 minutes or until the sauce thickens.
6. Mix the sour cream and sprinkle salt and pepper as needed.
7. Put pasta in the mushroom sauce and give a toss to combine. Use the pasta water if needed to make the sauce more liquid.
8. Serve in bowls with creamy sauce on top

Nutrition:

Calories: 447

Protein: 15 g

Fiber: 4 g

Carbohydrates: 66 g

Sugar: 5 g

Sodium: 127mg

Fat: 14 g

Tomato Basil Pasta

Preparation Time: 10 minutes

Cooking Time: 45 minutes

Servings: 6

Ingredients:

- ¾ teaspoon sea salt
- ½ cup extra-virgin olive oil
- 1 small chopped cherry tomato basket
- 2 finely chopped garlic cloves
- 1 oz. whole wheat pasta
- ½ cup chopped fresh basil
- Salt & pepper as needed

Directions:

1. Mix garlic, olive oil, and salt in a bowl.
2. Add 1 cup chopped cherry tomatoes to the olive oil bowl.
3. Allow it to rest for half an hour while stirring often.
4. Cook the pasta according to the guidelines.
5. Drain and reserve ½ pasta water.
6. Mix pasta and tomato mixture.
7. Serve with basil, a little pasta water for consistency, and salt & pepper.

Nutrition:

Calories: 448

Protein: 10 g

Fiber: 3 g

Carbohydrates: 58 g

Sugar: 3 g

Sodium: 300mg

Fat: 14

Creamy Lemon Garlic Pasta

Preparation Time: 10 minutes

Cooking Time: 20 minutes

Servings: 4

Ingredients:

- 1 head roasted garlic
- 8 oz. whole wheat pasta
- ¼ soaked & drained raw cashews
- ⅔ cup plant-based unsweetened milk
- ½ teaspoon lemon zest
- 4 tablespoons freshly squeezed lemon juice
- ½ tablespoon extra-virgin olive oil
- 1 thinly sliced onion
- 1 teaspoon nutritional yeast
- Salt & black pepper to taste

Directions:

1. Follow the package instructions to cook pasta.
2. Drain water, but don't rinse the pasta with water.
3. Add all the ingredients except oil, onion, and pasta to a blender and season with salt and pepper.
4. Blend everything until smooth.
5. Take a pan and heat oil over low heat
6. Stir in onion and sauté until tender.
7. Add the cashew mixture to the pan and stir until warm.
8. Fold pasta and cook on low until everything is warm and well combined.
9. Serve hot immediately!

Nutrition:

Calories: 342

Protein: 17 g

Fiber: 5 g

Carbohydrates: 54 g

Sugar: 26 g

Sodium: 420mg

Fat: 5 g

Creamy Chicken One Pot Pasta

Preparation Time: 35 minutes

Cooking Time: 5 minutes

Servings: 5

Ingredients:

- 1 pound boneless, skinless chicken thighs
- 8 oz. whole-wheat linguine/spaghetti
- 4 cups sliced mushrooms
- 4 cups water
- 2 cups sliced Brussels sprouts
- 1 medium chopped onion
- 4 thinly sliced garlic cloves
- 2 tablespoons chopped fresh chives
- 2 tablespoons Boursin cheese
- 1 ¼ teaspoons dried thyme
- ¾ teaspoon dried rosemary
- ¾ teaspoon salt

Directions:

1. Place a large pot of water over high heat.
2. Include pasta, chicken, Brussels sprouts, mushrooms, onion, garlic, 1 tablespoon cheese, 1 tablespoon chives, rosemary, thyme, and salt in the water.
3. Give it all a mix and bring it to a boil.
4. Stir occasionally until the water evaporates in 10-15 minutes.
5. Take the pot off the heat and let it rest for a few minutes.
6. Serve the pasta on plates with a dash of the remaining tablespoon of chives and cheese on top.

Nutrition:

Calories: 353

Protein: 27 g

Fiber: 8 g

Carbohydrates: 42 g

Sugar: 4 g

Sodium: 461mg

Fat: 10 g

Burrata Pasta With Cherry Tomatoes

Preparation Time: 10 minutes

Cooking Time: 20 minutes

Servings: 4

Ingredients:

- 8 oz. whole-wheat fettuccine
- 8 oz. burrata cheese
- 3 cups halved cherry tomatoes
- 3 cups packed baby spinach
- ¼ cup extra-virgin olive oil
- ¼ cup chopped fresh basil, more for garnish
- 1 ½ tablespoons chopped garlic
- ½ teaspoon unsalted Italian seasoning
- ½ teaspoon crushed red pepper
- ¼ teaspoon salt
- ¼ teaspoon ground pepper

Directions:

1. Put a large saucepan filled with water over high heat.
2. Bring the pasta to a boil and cook it according to the package details.
3. Reserve ½ cup pasta water, drain well, and set aside.
4. Heat oil over medium heat in a large, high-sided skillet.
5. Add and stir crushed red pepper, Italian seasoning, and garlic, and cook for a minute or two until fragrant.
6. Add in tomatoes, stir, and cook for 8-10 minutes until the tomatoes become mushy and saucy.
7. Add salt and pepper and remove the pan from heat.
8. Mix pasta and the reserved water into the tomato skillet and toss to coat.
9. Add in spinach and basil and toss to coat.
10. Return the skillet to medium flame and cook for 2 minutes until the pasta is mixed correctly and the spinach has wilted.
11. Cut or tear the burrata into pieces and stir in the pasta.
12. Divide the pasta among serving plates and garnish with more basil to serve.

Nutrition

Calories: 498

Protein: 20 g

Fiber: 7 g

Carbohydrates: 49 g

Sugar: 5 g

Sodium: 344mg

Fat: 30 g

Cheese & Beet Fettuccine Pasta

Preparation Time: 10 minutes
Cooking Time: 15 minutes
Servings: 4

Ingredients:

- 12 oz. whole-wheat fettuccine
- 1 (6.5 oz.) package garlic-herb marinated baby beets
- 4 oz. creamy low-fat cheese, divided
- ¼ cup toasted walnuts, coarsely chopped
- ¼ cup chopped fresh basil
- 6 tablespoons water
- 2 tablespoons extra-virgin olive oil
- 1 tablespoon white miso
- 1 tablespoon lemon zest
- ¼ teaspoon salt
- ¼ teaspoon ground pepper

Instructions:

1. Place a large pot of water over a high flame and bring to a boil.
2. Cook fettuccine as instructed in the package details.
3. Save ½ cup pasta water, drain well, and set pasta and reserved water aside.
4. Add beets with oil, water, lemon zest, and 2 oz of cheese, salt, and pepper in a blender.
5. Blend for a minute until smooth.
6. Crumble the rest of the 2 oz of cheese and leave aside.
7. Transfer the blended sauce to a large skillet over medium flame and let it simmer.
8. Toss in the pasta carefully while slowly adding the reserved pasta water, a tablespoon at a time, to reach the desired consistency.
9. Toss to combine and divide the pasta among serving bowls.
10. Garnish with walnuts, basil, and crumbled cheese, and serve immediately.

Nutrition (Per Serving):

Calories: 474
Protein: 20 g
Fiber: 11 g
Carbohydrates: 51 g
Sugar: 5 g
Sodium: 427mg
Fat: 20 g

Creamy Brussels Sprouts Fettuccine

Preparation Time: 10 minutes
Cooking Time: 20 minutes
Servings: 6
Ingredients:
- 12 oz. whole-wheat fettuccine
- 4 cups sliced mixed mushrooms, cremini/oyster/shiitake
- 4 cups thinly sliced Brussels sprouts
- 2 cups low-fat milk
- 1 cup finely shredded cheddar cheese, extra for garnish
- ½ cup vinegar
- 2 tablespoons all-purpose flour
- 1 tablespoon extra-virgin olive oil
- 1 tablespoon minced garlic
- ½ teaspoon salt
- ½ teaspoon freshly ground pepper

Directions:
1. Place a large pot of water over high heat and bring it to a boil.
2. Cook pasta for 8-10 minutes per the package directions.
3. Drain well, return to the pot, and set aside for use later.
4. Place a large skillet over medium flame and heat oil.
5. Stir in mushrooms and Brussels sprouts to cook for 8-10 minutes until the mushrooms get mushy.
6. Stir in garlic for a minute and add vinegar.
7. Scrape any brown bits in there and let it reach a boil.
8. Then, cook for a whole minute.
9. Mix flour and milk in a bowl and add to the skillet with salt and pepper.
10. Cook for 2 minutes while stirring until the sauce bubbles and thickens.
11. Mix in cheese until it melts, and add the mixture to the pasta.
12. Toss to combine and serve immediately with extra cheese.

Nutrition
Calories: 384
Protein: 18 g
Fiber: 10 g
Carbohydrates:56 g
Sugar: 8 g
Sodium: 431mg
Fat: 10 g

Kale Pesto Noodles

Preparation Time: 15 minutes
Cooking Time: 12 minutes
Servings: 1
Ingredients:
- ¼ cup oil
- 1 bunch kale
- ½ cup walnuts
- 2 cups fresh basil
- 1 spiralized zucchini
- Asparagus as needed
- 2 freshly squeezed limes
- Salt & pepper as needed
- Spinach leaves as needed
- Cherry tomatoes as needed

Directions:
1. Set the walnuts to soak in water overnight.
2. Next day, pulse the walnuts with the remaining ingredients except zucchini, spinach leaves, cherry tomatoes, and asparagus.
3. Mix well and add it to the asparagus, cherry tomatoes, and spinach leaves on top.

Nutrition:
Calories: 176
Protein: 7 g
Fiber: 4 g
Carbohydrates:5 g
Sugar: 8 g
Sodium: 413mg
Fat: 17 g

Arugula Pesto Pasta

Preparation Time: 10 minutes
Cooking Time: 10 minutes
Servings: 4

Ingredients:

- 3 garlic cloves
- ⅓ cup walnut pieces
- 8 oz. linguine noodles
- 2 cups packed basil leaves
- ¼ cup extra-virgin olive oil
- 2 cups packed arugula leaves
- Freshly ground black pepper as needed

Directions:

1. Add water to a pot, fill it halfway, and let it boil.
2. Cook noodles according to the package directions and drain.
3. Process walnuts, arugula, garlic, and basil until roughly grounded.
4. Add olive oil to the mix as the processor runs, and sprinkle pepper.
5. Combine and toss the noodles with this mix, and serve immediately!

Nutrition:

Calories: 360
Protein: 10 g
Fiber: 4 g
Carbohydrates: 58 g
Sugar: 3 g
Sodium: 187mg
Fat: 38 g

Vegetable Orzo Pasta

Preparation Time: 10 minutes
Cooking Time: 25 minutes
Servings: 6

Ingredients:

- 15.5 oz. can drained & rinsed black beans
- 10 oz. can of diced tomatoes
- 2 tablespoons extra-virgin olive oil
- 1 diced red bell pepper
- 1 diced green bell pepper
- 3 minced garlic cloves
- 1 diced yellow onion
- 2 teaspoons ground cumin
- 1 teaspoon chili powder
- Sea salt as needed
- Black pepper as needed
- Green chilies
- 1 ½ cups frozen corn
- 3 ½ cups low-sodium vegetable broth
- 16 oz. orzo pasta

Directions:

1. Put olive oil in a large pot over medium-high heat and heat until glossy.
2. Sauté in onion, garlic, red and green bell pepper for 5 minutes or until soft and fragrant.
3. Mix cumin, chili powder, salt, and pepper until combined.
4. Stir in black beans, diced tomatoes, green chilies, corn, and orzo.
5. Gradually pour the vegetable stock and bring it to a boil.
6. Change the heat to low-medium, put the lid on, and let simmer until the pasta is cooked and the liquid has vanished.
7. Give it 13 minutes and stir occasionally.
8. Serve immediately and enjoy!

Nutrition:

Calories: 86
Protein: 2 g
Fiber: 4 g
Carbohydrates: 16 g
Sugar: 1 g
Sodium: 40mg
Fat: 2 g

Crumbly Spaghetti Fritters

Preparation Time: 25 minutes

Cooking Time: 3 hours

Servings: 10

Ingredients:

- 10 oz. cooked whole wheat pasta
- ½ cup breadcrumbs
- F4 oz. Low-fat cheese
- 4 teaspoons sesame oil
- 1 teaspoon paprika
- 1 teaspoon ground black pepper
- 1 teaspoon salt
- 3 eggs

Directions:

1. Chop pasta and coat with the breadcrumbs.
2. Whisk eggs and add them to the pasta mixture.
3. Mix the remaining breadcrumbs, black pepper, and salt.
4. Grease your hands with sesame oil to prevent the mixture from sticking and forming small fritters.
5. Place them in the slow cooker and cover.
6. Cook on high for 2 hours.
7. After, flip the patties and cook for another hour on high.
8. Remove the patties and allow to cool.
9. Serve with your favorite sauce.

Nutrition:

Calories: 177

Protein: 9 g

Fiber: 2 g

Carbohydrates: 12 g

Sugar: 0 g

Sodium: 97mg

Fat: 2 g

Macaroni With Low-Fat Cheese

Preparation Time: 15 minutes

Cooking Time: 2 hours

Servings: 8

Ingredients:

- 1 cup cayenne pepper sauce
- 3 medium peeled & shredded carrots
- Thinly sliced celery
- Multigrain rotini pasta
- Dry salad dressing mix
- American less-fat cheese

Directions:

1. Cut the cheese into bite-sized pieces.
2. Grease the slow cooker with butter and add all the ingredients except cheese.
3. Stir, cover, and cook until the pasta absorbs all the liquid on high.
4. Five minutes before completion, add cheese on top and don't mix.
5. Serve and enjoy!

Nutrition:

Calories: 307

Protein: 14 g

Fiber: 2 g

Carbohydrates: 39 g

Sugar: 12 g

Sodium: 391mg

Fat: 11 g

Tuna Mushroom Noodles

Preparation Time: 5 minutes
Cooking Time: 2 hours
Servings: 4

Ingredients:

- 3 cups water
- 16 oz. egg noodles
- 1 cup frozen peas
- ¼ cup breadcrumbs
- 28 oz. mushroom soup cream
- 14 oz. drained canned tuna
- 4 oz. grated less-fat cheddar cheese

Directions:

1. Add all the ingredients except breadcrumbs and cheese into the crock pot.
2. Cover and cook for an hour on high.
3. Sprinkle breadcrumbs and cheese and cook for another hour on high.
4. Serve immediately and enjoy!

Nutrition:

Calories: 251
Protein: 12 g
Fiber: 1 g
Carbohydrates: 20 g
Sugar: 4 g
Sodium: 573mg
Fat: 6 g

CHAPTER 3:
HEARTY BEAN DISHES

Healthy Chickpea Bowl

Preparation Time: 10 minutes

Cooking Time: 30 minutes

Servings: 4

Ingredients:

- 15 oz. can drained chickpeas
- 1 chopped red onion
- 1 teaspoon curry powder
- Sea salt and black pepper as needed
- ½ cup baby spinach
- 1 pitted, peeled & sliced avocado
- 2 teaspoons ground turmeric
- 1 tablespoon extra-virgin olive oil

Directions:

1. Take a baking sheet and line it with parchment paper.
2. Set the oven to 350 degrees Fahrenheit.
3. Spread chickpeas and the rest of the ingredients except spinach on the baking sheet.
4. Bake for 30 minutes until golden brown and soft.
5. Divide the chickpeas between bowls, toss, and serve with spinach.

Nutrition:

Calories: 230

Protein: 7 g

Fiber: 7 g

Carbohydrates: 7 g

Sugar: 5 g

Sodium: 277mg

Fat: 5 g

Cucumber and Chickpea Bowl

Preparation time: 10 minutes

Cooking time: 0 minutes

Servings: 4

Ingredients:

- 1 cup cubed cucumber
- 1 cup drained chickpeas
- 1 cup halved cherry tomatoes
- ¼ cup lemon juice
- ⅓ cup tahini paste
- ¼ teaspoon ground coriander
- 3 tablespoons extra-virgin olive oil
- 1 tablespoon lime juice
- 1 minced garlic clove
- Sea salt and black pepper as needed

Directions:

1. Mix all the ingredients in a bowl, toss, and divide into smaller bowls.
2. Serve immediately!

Nutrition:

Calories: 182

Protein: 6 g

Fiber: 73 g

Carbohydrates: 4 g

Sugar: 2 g

Sodium: 623mg

Fat: 4 g

Fulfilling Beans Mix

Preparation Time: 10 minutes
Cooking Time: 15 minutes
Servings: 4
Ingredients:

- ½ teaspoon garlic powder
- ½ teaspoon smoked paprika
- 2 teaspoons chili powder
- 1 tablespoon extra-virgin olive oil
- 1 tablespoon chopped oregano
- 1 tablespoon chopped dill
- 1 ½ cups cooked black beans
- 1 cup cooked red kidney beans
- 1 cup chopped corn kernels
- 1 ½ cups cooked chickpeas
- 1 teaspoon garam masala
- 1 chopped red bell pepper
- 2 chopped tomatoes
- 1 cup chopped cashews
- ½ cup vegetable stock
- 1 tablespoon balsamic vinegar

Directions:

1. Heat oil in a pan over medium flame.
2. Add all the ingredients, stir, and cook for 15 minutes.
3. Divide between plates and make sure they are well combined.
4. Serve immediately!

Nutrition:
Calories: 300
Protein: 13 g
Fiber: 3 g
Carbohydrates: 6 g
Sugar: 3 g
Sodium: 32mg
Fat: 8 g

Green Bean Fries

Preparation Time: 10 minutes
Cooking Time: 8 hours
Servings: 8
Ingredients:

- ⅓ cup avocado oil
- 5 oz. trimmed green beans
- 1 teaspoon garlic powder
- 1 teaspoon onion powder
- 1 teaspoon turmeric powder
- Sea salt and black pepper to taste
- 1 teaspoon dried oregano
- 1 teaspoon dried mint

Directions:

1. Add all the ingredients to a bowl and toss to combine.
2. Dry the mixture in a dehydrator for 8 hours.
3. Serve cold as a side.

Nutrition:
Calories: 100
Protein: 5 g
Fiber: 4 g
Carbohydrates: 8 g
Sugar: 8 g
Sodium: 1180mg
Fat: 12 g

Yummy Lentil Cakes

Preparation Time: 10 minutes

Cooking Time: 10 minutes

Servings: 8

Ingredients:

- 2 teaspoons dried basil
- 1 cup chopped yellow onion
- 1 cup chopped leeks
- ¼ cup chopped parsley
- 1 tablespoon curry powder
- ¼ cup chopped cilantro
- 1 cup canned, drained & rinsed red lentils
- 1 teaspoon ground coriander
- 2 tablespoons coconut flour
- 1 tablespoon extra-virgin olive oil

Directions:

1. Use a potato masher to mash lentils in a bowl.
2. Add all the ingredients except oil and stir.
3. Shape cakes out of the lentil mixture.
4. Heat up oil in a pan over a medium-high flame.
5. Cook cakes for 5 minutes on each side until golden brown.
6. Serve hot!

Nutrition:

Calories: 142

Protein: 4 g

Fiber: 3 g

Carbohydrates: 8 g

Sugar: 2 g

Sodium: 188mg

Fat: 4 g

Vegetable Minestrone

Preparation Time: 15 minutes

Cooking Time: 25 minutes

Servings: 4

Ingredients:

- 3 minced garlic cloves
- 2 peeled & diced carrots
- 1 diced celery stalk
- 1 ½ tablespoons extra-virgin olive oil
- 1 diced onion
- ⅛ teaspoon freshly ground black pepper
- ¼ teaspoon dried thyme
- 7 cups low-sodium vegetable stock
- 2 bay leaves
- ¼ teaspoon red pepper flakes
- 4 oz. whole wheat pasta
- 4 cups fresh baby spinach
- ¼ cup freshly squeezed lemon juice
- 2 medium sliced zucchini
- ¼ cup chopped fresh parsley

Directions:

1. Take a stockpot and heat the oil.
2. Add onion, garlic, celery, and carrots, and cook until onion becomes tender.
3. Next, add black pepper, thyme, bay leaf, and chili flakes, and cook for a minute until you start smelling the aroma.
4. Pour in the vegetable stock, stir, and boil.
5. Add pasta, reduce heat to a simmer, and cook for 12 minutes or until al dente.
6. Next, put in zucchini and cook for another 2 minutes.
7. Lastly, stir in the spinach and lemon juice for 2 minutes.
8. Top with parsley and serve in bowls.

Nutrition:

Calories: 217

Protein: 5 g

Fiber: 5 g

Carbohydrates: 36 g

Sugar: 4 g

Sodium: 578mg

Fat: 6 g

Quick Peas Mash

Preparation Time: 10 minutes
Cooking Time: 20 minutes
Servings: 4

Ingredients:
- 1 oz. green peas
- 1 cup water
- 1 teaspoon curry powder
- 1 teaspoon dried mint
- 2 tablespoons soft coconut butter
- ½ cup coconut milk
- A pinch of sea salt and black pepper
- 1 tablespoon chopped chives

Directions:
1. Add water, salt, pepper, and peas to a pot.
2. Boil over medium heat and reduce to a simmer for 20 minutes.
3. Drain and transfer to a blender with the remaining ingredients.
4. Blend until smooth and divide between small bowls.
5. Serve immediately with whole wheat bread!

Nutrition:
Calories: 188
Protein: 4 g
Fiber: 4 g
Carbohydrates: 5 g
Sugar: 9 g
Sodium: 118mg
Fat: 5 g

Chickpea Turmeric Stew

Preparation Time: 10 minutes
Cooking Time: 30 minutes
Servings: 4

Ingredients:
- 1 finely chopped jalapenos
- 3 minced garlic cloves
- 1 small diced white onion
- 1 tablespoon minced ginger
- 1 tablespoon coconut oil
- ½ tablespoon mild curry powder
- ½ teaspoon dried turmeric
- 2 teaspoon soy sauce
- 1 14 oz. can full-fat coconut milk
- ½ cup pure pineapple juice
- 1 small cubed sweet potato
- 1 small cubed potato
- 1 ½ cups cooked, rinsed & drained chickpeas
- 2 tablespoons fresh lime juice
- Sea salt as needed

Directions:
1. Place a pan over medium flame and heat oil.
2. Stir in onion with a dash of salt and cook for a minute or until translucent.
3. Put in pepper, garlic, ginger, turmeric, and salt to taste.
4. Stir for another 7 minutes until the onion is soft.
5. Add in curry powder, give it a stir, and let it sit for a minute.
6. Next, put in milk, juice, water, and soy sauce with both sweet and plain potatoes.
7. Add a dash of salt, stir, and bring the mixture to a boil.
8. Reduce the heat to a simmer and let it cook for 15 or until the potatoes are tender.
9. You may mash some potatoes to thicken up the consistency.
10. Add in the cooked chickpeas and lime juice and let it simmer for five more minutes.
11. Once everything is mixed, ladle the stew into bowls.
12. Serve hot and enjoy!

Nutrition:
Calories: 306
Protein: 7 g
Fiber: 7 g
Carbohydrates: 38 g
Sugar: 9 g
Sodium: 586mg
Fat: 15 g

Herb White Beans Stew

Preparation Time: 10 minutes
Cooking Time: 50 minutes
Servings: 6
Ingredients:

- 4 cups water
- 1 cup soaked white beans
- 1 tablespoon avocado oil
- 1 cup chopped zucchini
- 1 cup vegetable broth
- 1 teaspoon tomato paste
- ½ teaspoon ground black pepper
- ½ teaspoon peppercorns
- ¼ teaspoon ground nutmeg

Directions:

1. Take a saucepan and heat avocado oil on medium-high flame.
2. Add zucchini and cook for 5 minutes.
3. Add the rest of the ingredients, bring to a boil, and reduce heat to a simmer for 50 minutes.
4. Once everything is cooked and well combined, ladle out into bowls and serve.

Nutrition:

Calories: 184
Protein: 12 g
Fiber: 8 g
Carbohydrates: 32 g
Sugar: 2 g
Sodium: 37mg
Fat: 1 g

Chipotle Kidney Beans Burrito Bowl

Preparation Time: 15 minutes
Cooking Time: 15 minutes
Servings: 2
Ingredients:

- 1 tablespoon extra-virgin olive oil
- 125g brown rice
- 1 tablespoon apple cider vinegar
- 400g drained & rinsed red kidney beans
- 1 teaspoon pure maple syrup
- 100g chopped curly kale
- 2 chopped garlic cloves
- 1 halved & sliced avocado
- 1 tablespoon chipotle paste
- 1 medium chopped tomato
- 1 small, chopped onion

Directions:

1. Cook the rice by following the package guidelines, drain it, and keep it warm in the pan.
2. Heat oil in a frying pan and stir in garlic until golden brown.
3. Stir in beans, vinegar, chipotle, and maple syrup for 2 minutes.
4. In a separate pan, boil the kale for a minute, drain, and squeeze until no water remains.
5. Divide the rice into separate bowls.
6. Serve with the bean mixture, kale, tomato, onion, and avocado for a fulfilling lunch.

Nutrition:

Calories: 573
Protein: 16 g
Fiber: 15 g
Carbohydrates: 72 g
Sugar: 7 g
Sodium: 0mg
Fat: 21 g

Sweet Potato & Black Bean Chilli

Preparation Time: 5 minutes

Cooking Time: 20 minutes

Servings: 4

Ingredients:

- 1 large peeled & diced sweet potato
- 4 minced garlic cloves
- 1 tablespoon & 2 teaspoons extra-virgin olive oil
- 4 teaspoons ground cumin
- 1 large diced onion
- 2 tablespoons chili powder
- 2 ½ cups water
- 14 oz. diced tomatoes can
- ¼ teaspoon sea salt
- 15 oz. can of rinsed black beans
- ½ cup fresh cilantro
- 4 teaspoons lime juice
- ½ teaspoon ground chipotle chile

Directions:

1. Place a Dutch pan over medium flame and heat oil.
2. Add in sweet potato and onion, and stir until onions are soft.
3. Stir in cumin, garlic, salt, chili powder, and chipotle, and continue stirring for half a minute.
4. Lower the heat to a simmer, cover the sweet potato, and let it cook for 12 minutes or until tender.
5. Add beans, tomatoes, and lemon juice.
6. Increase the heat to a boil, stirring occasionally.
7. Lower heat and bring to a gentle simmer for five minutes.
8. Remove from heat, transfer to bowls, and serve with cilantro.

Nutrition:

Calories: 323

Protein: 12 g

Fiber: 15 g

Carbohydrates: 54 g

Sugar: 13 g

Sodium: 573mg

Fat: 7 g

Black-Eyed Peas Dip

Preparation Time: 10 minutes

Cooking Time: 0 minutes

Servings: 8

Ingredients:

- 2 cups canned, drained & rinsed black-eyed peas
- ½ teaspoon garlic powder
- 1 teaspoon Italian seasoning
- ½ teaspoon chili powder
- ½ cup coconut cream
- A pinch of sea salt & black pepper
- ½ teaspoon chili sauce
- 1 teaspoon hot paprika

Directions:

1. Add all the ingredients to a blender.
2. Blend until smooth and serve as a side.
3. Serve with whole wheat bread or vegetable fries.

Nutrition:

Calories: 127

Protein: 8 g

Fiber: 7 g

Carbohydrates: 18 g

Sugar: 1 g

Sodium: 65mg

Fat: 5 g

Italian Bean Chicken

Preparation Time: 10 minutes
Cooking Time: 3 hours
Servings: 4

Ingredients:

- 4 chicken breasts
- 1 jar spaghetti sauce
- 1 oz. green beans
- 8 oz. sliced mushrooms
- 1 teaspoon Italian seasoning

Directions:

1. Add all the ingredients to the slow cooker.
2. Cover and cook for 3 hours on high.
3. Once done, serve and enjoy!

Nutrition:

Calories: 340
Protein: 32 g
Fiber: 10 g
Carbohydrates: 36 g
Sugar: 1 g
Sodium: 890mg
Fat: 9 g

Vegetables & Lentil Stew

Preparation Time: 20 minutes
Cooking Time: 35 minutes
Servings: 4

Ingredients:

- 2 large roughly-chopped carrots
- 2 medium thinly sliced leeks
- 1 large unpeeled & chopped into cubes sweet potato
- 3 garlic minced cloves
- 6 cups water
- 4 cups chopped hearty greens, kale/Swiss chard
- 1 ½ cups green/brown lentils
- 2 tablespoons extra-virgin olive oil, divided
- 2 tablespoons tomato paste
- 1 ½ teaspoons ground cumin
- 1 ¼ teaspoons white miso
- ½ teaspoon salt

Directions:

1. Place a large Dutch oven or stockpot over medium-high heat with a tablespoon of oil.
2. Stir in sweet potato and cook for 6-8 minutes until lightly browned and soft.
3. Stir in leeks and carrots and cook for 3-4 minutes until soft.
4. Stir in cumin, tomato paste, miso, garlic, and a tablespoon of oil.
5. Stir constantly for a minute until fragrant and tomato paste becomes darkened.
6. Pour in water, add lentils with salt, raise the flame to high, and bring it to a boil.
7. Lower heat to a simmer on medium-low and cover to cook for 25 minutes until the lentils are tender.
8. Stir in the greens, cover, and cook for 10 minutes more until the greens are wilted.
9. Dish out and serve immediately.

Nutrition:

Calories: 451
Protein: 22 g
Fiber: 13 g
Carbohydrates: 77 g
Sugar: 9 g
Sodium: 475mg
Fat: 8 g

One Pot Chickpea Curry

Preparation Time: 25 minutes

Cooking Time: 20 minutes

Servings: 6

Ingredients:

- 15 oz. can salt-free and rinsed chickpeas
- 14 oz. can coconut milk
- 2 medium chopped tomatoes
- 1 large chopped onion
- 2 large minced garlic cloves
- 1 medium cubed sweet potato
- 1 ½ cups 1-inch cut green beans
- 1 cup low-sodium vegetable broth
- ½ cup chopped cilantro
- 2 tablespoons avocado oil
- 2 tablespoons lime juice
- 1 tablespoon minced fresh ginger
- 1 tablespoon curry powder
- 1 teaspoon cumin seeds
- 1 teaspoon mustard seeds
- ¼ teaspoon crushed red pepper
- ¾ teaspoon salt

Directions:

1. Place a large saucepan over medium heat with oil.
2. Stir in cumin and mustard seeds and cook for 30 seconds to a minute until they start to pop.
3. Stir onions and cook for 3 minutes.
4. Stir in ginger, garlic, crushed red pepper, curry powder, and salt.
5. Cook for a minute until fragrant.
6. Add in coconut milk and broth, and add tomatoes, sweet potato, green beans, and chickpeas.
7. Increase heat to bring it to a boil and then lower to a simmer.
8. Cook without cover for 15 minutes while stirring frequently until the veggies become tender.
9. Take off the heat and stir in lemon juice and cilantro.
10. Dish out to serve immediately.

Nutrition:

Calories: 312

Protein: 7 g

Fiber: 8 g

Carbohydrates: 30 g

Sugar: 9 g

Sodium: 436mg

Fat: 21 g

Chapter 4:
Lean Meats & Poultry

Avocado Chicken Wraps

Preparation Time: 10 minutes
Cooking Time: 0 minutes
Servings: 4
Ingredients:

- 2 green onions
- ¾ teaspoon cumin
- ¼ teaspoon coriander
- 1 teaspoon lime juice
- ½ teaspoon kosher salt
- 2 cups shredded chicken
- 4 flour tortillas as needed
- ½ teaspoon garlic powder
- 1 ½ teaspoon chili powder
- 1 teaspoon smoked paprika
- 1 cup chopped grape tomatoes
- 3 tablespoons chopped cilantro
- 3 half-cut & pits-removed avocados
- ¼ teaspoon freshly ground black pepper

Directions:

1. Scoop out the avocado flesh, add to a bowl, and mash it until smooth.
2. Mix in the remaining ingredients except tortillas and combine well.
3. Add the mixture to the tortillas and wrap them closed.
4. Serve once done, and enjoy!

Nutrition:
Calories: 374
Protein: 21 g
Fiber: 8 g
Carbohydrates: 16 g
Sugar: 5 g
Sodium: 899mg
Fat: 27 g

Chicken Avocado Cups

Preparation Time: 5 minutes
Cooking Time: 0 minutes
Servings: 3
Ingredients:

- 1 teaspoon lime juice
- ½ teaspoon chili powder
- 3 (6 oz.) canned & drained chicken
- 1 tablespoon finely chopped cilantro
- 3 halved-lengthwise & pitted avocados

Directions:

1. Combine all the ingredients except avocados and lime juice.
2. Spoon the chicken mixture into the avocados and drizzle lemon juice.
3. Serve once done, and enjoy!

Nutrition:
Calories: 601
Protein: 41 g
Fiber: 8 g
Carbohydrates: 18 g
Sugar: 1 g
Sodium: 864mg
Fat: 43 g

Chicken Jambalaya

Preparation Time: 10 minutes
Cooking Time: 20 minutes
Servings: 1

Ingredients:

- ⅓ cup chopped celery
- ¼ cup dry breadcrumbs
- Salt & pepper as needed
- ½ cup stewed tomatoes
- 1 chopped medium onion
- 12.5 oz. can chunk chicken
- 1 cup uncooked brown rice
- 2 tablespoons melted butter
- 2 teaspoons Cajun seasoning
- ¼ cup chopped green bell peppers
- 4 tablespoons dehydrated green onions

Directions:

1. Start by preheating the oven to 350 degrees Fahrenheit and grease a 1.8-liter casserole dish with oil.
2. Combine chicken, rice, and tomatoes in a saucepan over medium heat and let it simmer covered for 10 minutes.
3. Stir in the green onions, onion, celery, Cajun seasoning, salt, and pepper and mix well.
4. Combine breadcrumbs and butter in a separate bowl and mix well.
5. Transfer the jambalaya to a baking dish, cover with the breadcrumbs, and bake it for an hour.
6. Slice and serve once cooked.

Nutrition:

Calories: 285
Protein: 21 g
Fiber: 4 g
Carbohydrates: 41 g
Sugar: 4 g
Sodium: 654mg
Fat: 4 g

Tasty Chicken Sticks

Preparation Time: 10 minutes
Cooking Time: 20 minutes
Servings: 4

Ingredients:

- Cilantro as needed
- 1 teaspoon meat tenderizer
- 4 boneless & skinless chicken breasts halves

Directions:

1. Start by washing the chicken under running water and pat dry with a paper towel.
2. Toss chicken and meat tenderizer in a bowl and let it rest for an hour or a half.
3. Meanwhile, heat the grill to medium-high and grill the chicken for 5-10 minutes from both sides.
4. Serve with cilantro and herbs you like on top!

Nutrition:

Calories: 218
Protein: 27 g
Fiber: 2 g
Carbohydrates: 3 g
Sugar: 0 g
Sodium: 314mg
Fat: 9 g

Chicken Skewers

Preparation Time: 10 minutes
Cooking Time: 20 minutes
Servings: 4

Ingredients:

- 8 Skewers
- ¾ cup low-sodium soy sauce
- ¾ cup brown sugar
- ½ cup pineapple juice
- 2 minced garlic cloves
- ½ teaspoon minced ginger
- 2 (cut 1-inch pieces) pounds of boneless chicken

Directions:

1. Combine all the ingredients except the skewers in a bowl and let the chicken marinate for an hour.
2. Meanwhile, oil the grill and heat it to medium-high.
3. Thread the chicken onto the skewers and grill each side for 3 to 5 minutes.
4. Serve once done, and enjoy with salad!

Nutrition:

Calories: 502
Protein: 56 g
Fiber: 2 g
Carbohydrates: 48 g
Sugar: 13 g
Sodium: 688mg
Fat: 8 g

Sesame Chicken Wings

Preparation Time: 15 minutes
Cooking Time: 9 hours
Servings: 5

Ingredients:

- 1 teaspoon salt
- 1 tablespoon honey
- 1 oz. chicken wings
- 1 teaspoon mustard
- 1 tablespoon low-fat butter
- 1 teaspoon oregano
- 1 teaspoon cilantro
- 1 tablespoon sesame seeds
- 1 teaspoon cayenne pepper

Directions:

1. Mix all the ingredients together and transfer to the slow cooker.
2. Cover with the lid and cook on low for 9 hours.
3. Remove the wings once done, and serve hot with your favorite sauce.

Nutrition:

Calories: 160
Protein: 20 g
Fiber: 0 g
Carbohydrates: 4 g
Sugar: 12 g
Sodium: 942mg
Fat: 6 g

Grilled Chicken Breasts

Preparation Time: 15 minutes
Cooking Time: 30 minutes
Servings: 4

Ingredients:

- ½ cup lemon juice
- Seasoning salt as needed
- 2 teaspoons dried parsley
- ½ teaspoon onion powder
- Ground black pepper as needed
- 4 skinless & boneless chicken breast halves

Directions:

1. Begin by preheating an outdoor grill at medium-high heat and oil it.
2. Combine the ingredients together in a bowl and discard the lemon juice.
3. Cook the chicken on the hot grill for 10 to 15 minutes from both sides until cooked through and juices run clear.
4. Serve once done, and enjoy!

Nutrition:

Calories: 139
Protein: 27 g
Fiber: 0 g
Carbohydrates: 3 g
Sugar: 0 g
Sodium: 958mg
Fat: 1 g

Grilled Chicken Thighs

Preparation Time: 15 minutes
Cooking Time: 15 minutes
Servings: 6

Ingredients:

- Salt as needed
- ¼ cup fresh lime juice
- 2 tablespoons canola oil
- Black pepper as needed
- ½ cup fresh orange juice
- 24 metal/bamboo skewers
- 2 tablespoons chili powder
- 3 coarsely chopped garlic cloves
- 6 boneless, skinless, & cut-half-lengthwise chicken thighs

Directions:

1. Combine all the ingredients together except the skewers in a bowl and allow the chicken to stay in the marination for an hour or 4.
2. Meanwhile, grease the grill with oil and heat it to medium-high.
3. Thread the chicken onto the skewers and grill each side for 3 to 5 minutes.
4. Serve once done and enjoy with sauce.

Nutrition:

Calories: 113
Protein: 14 g
Fiber: 0 g
Carbohydrates: 2 g
Sugar: 20 g
Sodium: 256mg
Fat: 5 g

Chicken & Cabbage Stir-Fry

Preparation Time: 10 minutes
Cooking Time: 10 minutes
Servings: 4

Ingredients:

- ¼ cup water
- 1 teaspoon avocado oil
- 1 tablespoon cornstarch
- 1 teaspoon ground ginger
- ½ teaspoon garlic powder
- 3 cups thinly sliced green cabbage
- Freshly ground black pepper as needed
- 10 oz. boneless, skinless & thinly sliced chicken breast

Directions:

1. Cook the chicken in a skillet over medium-high flame until browned.
2. Stir in the cabbage until crispy, tender, and green.
3. Meanwhile, combine garlic, ginger, cornstarch, and water together in a bowl and add to the pan.
4. Continue stirring until the sauce starts to thicken, and season with pepper.
5. Serve with rice, and enjoy!

Nutrition:

Calories: 256
Protein: 27 g
Fiber: 6 g
Carbohydrates: 17 g
Sugar: 9 g
Sodium: 199mg
Fat: 10 g

Turkey & Swiss Sandwich

Preparation Time: 10 minutes
Cooking Time: 5 minutes
Servings: 1

Ingredients:

- 2 slices low-fat Swiss cheese
- 1 tablespoon fat-free mayonnaise
- 2 slices thick-cut rye bread

Directions:

1. Place the rack 6 inches away from the heat and start by preheating the oven broiler.
2. Spread mayonnaise over one side of the bread slice, generously layer cheese, spinach, and turkey on top, and cover with the slice.
3. Place the sandwich on the baking dish and broil in the oven for 5 minutes until heated through.
4. Remove to serve immediately, and enjoy!

Nutrition:

Calories: 577
Protein: 38 g
Fiber: 38 g
Carbohydrates: 35 g
Sugar: 3 g
Sodium: 654mg
Fat: 32 g

Chicken Mushrooms Stroganoff

Preparation Time: 16 minutes
Cooking Time: 4 hours
Servings: 4

Ingredients:
- 1 cup chicken stock
- 1 cup coconut milk
- 2 minced garlic cloves
- ¼ teaspoon celery seeds
- 1 chopped yellow onion
- 1 ½ teaspoon dried thyme
- 2 tablespoons chopped parsley
- 8 oz. roughly chopped mushrooms
- 1 oz. cut into pieces boneless, skinless chicken breasts
- Salt & black pepper as needed
- Cooked whole wheat pasta as needed

Directions:
1. Combine all the ingredients in the crock pot.
2. Cover and cook on high for 4 hours.
3. Stir in pasta and sprinkle some leftover parsley.
4. Serve warm and enjoy!

Nutrition:
Calories: 364
Protein: 24 g
Fiber: 38 g
Carbohydrates: 14 g
Sugar: 3 g
Sodium: 760mg
Fat: 22 g

Latin Chicken

Preparation Time:10 minutes
Cooking Time: 5 hours
Servings: 6

Ingredients:
- 2 cups water
- 1 teaspoon salt
- 1 teaspoon chili flakes
- 21 oz. chicken thighs
- 1 petal-cut onion
- 1 teaspoon garlic powder
- ½ cup hot salsa
- ¼ cup frozen sweet corn
- 1 pitted & chopped peach
- 1 teaspoon avocado oil
- 6 oz. Julienned sweet pepper

Directions:
1. Add all the ingredients to the crock pot.
2. Cover and cook on high for 5 hours.
3. Serve immediately and enjoy!

Nutrition:
Calories: 182
Protein: 18 g
Fiber: 1 g
Carbohydrates: 7 g
Sugar: 9 g
Sodium: 483mg
Fat: 9 g

Baked Chicken Breast

Preparation Time: 10 minutes
Cooking Time: 23 minutes
Servings: 2

Ingredients:

- ½ cup olive oil
- 2 minced garlic cloves
- ½ cup fresh lemon juice
- ½ teaspoon dried thyme
- 1 teaspoon dried oregano
- 6 oz. Boneless, skinless chicken breasts
- Freshly ground black pepper & salt as needed

Directions:

1. Season chicken with salt and pepper in a bowl.
2. In another bowl, combine the remaining ingredients and pour over the chicken.
3. Marinate the chicken with the mixture and leave it in the marination for 15 minutes.
4. Remove the chicken and place it in the air fryer basket.
5. Cook for 15 minutes at 350 degrees Fahrenheit from both sides or until tender.
6. Serve once cooked, and enjoy!

Nutrition:

Calories: 466
Protein: 47 g
Fiber: 0 g
Carbohydrates: 3 g
Sugar: 0 g
Sodium: 570mg
Fat: 32 g

Herb Turkey Roast

Preparation Time: 10 minutes
Cooking Time: 40 minutes
Servings: 6

Ingredients:

- 1 crushed garlic clove
- Salt & pepper as needed
- 1 ½ tablespoons olive oil
- 1 finely chopped teaspoon fresh chives
- 1 finely chopped tablespoon fresh rosemary
- 2 ¾ oz. Bone & skin on split turkey breast

Directions:

1. Start by preheating the air fryer at 350 degrees Fahrenheit.
2. Combine herbs and seasonings in a bowl, add olive oil a little at a time, and mash these ingredients together until blended.
3. Soak moisture from the breast with a paper towel and marinate with the herb blend.
4. Arrange the breast skin-side down in the air fryer basket.
5. Cook for 20 minutes from both sides or until tender.
6. Remove to a plate and let cool before slicing to serve.

Nutrition:

Calories: 262
Protein: 39 g
Fiber: 0 g
Carbohydrates: 0 g
Sugar: 0 g
Sodium: 570mg
Fat: 10 g

Mushroom Turkey Meatballs

Preparation Time: 10 minutes

Cooking Time: 10 minutes

Servings: 4

Ingredients:

- Cooking spray as needed
- 1 teaspoon garlic powder
- 1 teaspoon onion powder
- 1 ¼ oz. ground turkey meat
- 6 cleaned & trimmed mushrooms
- Salt & ground black pepper as needed

Directions:

1. Puree mushrooms in a blender, sprinkle salt and pepper and pulse a few times.
2. Add turkey, the mushroom mixture, and the leftover ingredients except the cooking spray.
3. Mix and shape patties with your hands.
4. Oil the patties with olive oil cooking spray and arrange them in the air fryer basket.
5. Shut the lid and cook for 10 minutes at 320 degrees Fahrenheit.
6. Serve on plates and enjoy!

Nutrition:

Calories: 222

Protein: 4 g

Fiber: 0 g

Carbohydrates: 6 g

Sugar: 0 g

Sodium: 304mg

Fat: 4 g

CHAPTER 5:
NUTRITIOUS FISH & SEAFOOD

Lemon & Butter Salmon

Preparation Time: 10 minutes
Cooking Time: 10 minutes
Servings: 4
Ingredients:
- 1 tablespoon olive oil
- 3 tablespoons unsalted low-fat butter
- 2 tablespoons lemon juice
- 1 teaspoon grated lemon zest
- 2 tablespoons minced fresh rosemary
- Salt & ground black pepper as needed
- 4 (5 oz.) skin-on, boneless salmon fillets

Directions:
1. Sprinkle salt and pepper over fillets and heat up oil in a nonstick wok over medium flame.
2. Put the fillets with the skin side facing down and cook for 5 minutes without interruption.
3. Flip the fillets to the other uncooked side and cook for two minutes until done.
4. Combine the butter, lemon juice, zest, and rosemary in the pan thoroughly.
5. Spoon over the salmon to serve!

Nutrition:
Calories: 505
Protein: 43 g
Fiber: 3 g
Carbohydrates: 1 g
Sugar: 4 g
Sodium: 213mg
Fat: 35 g

Coconut Shrimp Kabobs

Preparation Time: 1 hour 20 minutes
Cooking Time: 5 minutes
Servings: 4
Ingredients:
- Olive oil as needed
- 2 teaspoons soy sauce
- ½ cup light coconut milk
- 1 tablespoon chopped cilantro
- ¼ cup freshly squeezed lime juice
- ¼ cup freshly squeezed orange juice
- 4 teaspoons red hot sauce
- ¾ pound cut-into-1-inch-pieces pineapple chunks
- 1 ½ pounds uncooked peeled & deveined jumbo shrimp

Directions:
1. Combine all the ingredients together except shrimp and pineapple in a bowl.
2. Toss shrimp in to coat, cover, and refrigerate for an hour in the marinade.
3. Thread the shrimp and pineapple onto the metal skewers and heat up the griddle at medium heat.
4. Put the skewers on the hot griddle top and cook them for 6 minutes from both sides, flipping once, until the shrimp change color to opaque pink.
5. Remove to the serving plates and serve!

Nutrition:
Calories: 165
Protein: 24 g
Fiber: 1 g
Carbohydrates: 12 g
Sugar: 7 g
Sodium: 240mg
Fat: 2 g

Easy Lemon Scallops

Preparation Time: 10 minutes
Cooking Time: 6 minutes
Servings: 4

Ingredients:

- 20 scallops
- 1 teaspoon salt
- 4 tablespoons olive oil
- 1 ½ tablespoon lemon pepper seasoning

Directions:

1. Put all the ingredients into a mixing bowl and mix well.
2. Cover the bowl, refrigerate for 30 minutes, and start heating the griddle at high heat.
3. Place the scallops on the hot griddle top to cook for 3 minutes from both sides.
4. Remove to serve once cooked and enjoy.

Nutrition:

Calories: 408
Protein: 38 g
Fiber: 3 g
Carbohydrates: 9 g
Sugar: 4 g
Sodium: 988mg
Fat: 24 g

Cornmeal Fish Fillets

Preparation Time: 10 minutes
Cooking Time: 10 minutes
Servings: 2

Ingredients:

- ¼ teaspoon kosher salt
- ¼ cup yellow cornmeal
- Lemon wedges as needed
- 2 teaspoons extra-virgin olive oil
- ⅛ teaspoon freshly ground pepper
- 4 (5 oz.) thin, white-fleshed fish fillets

Directions:

1. Put the cornmeal on a plate and sprinkle the fish with salt and pepper.
2. Cover the fillets with the cornmeal completely.
3. Meanwhile, heat the oil in a large nonstick skillet over medium flame, making sure the oil covers the bottom entirely.
4. Put the fish in to cook for 3 minutes from both sides, flipping once to cook both sides evenly.
5. Flake the fish with a fork to check the doneness. If it flakes easily, it's done.
6. Serve with lemon wedges, and enjoy!

Nutrition:

Calories: 166
Protein: 24 g
Fiber: 1 g
Carbohydrates: 5 g
Sugar: 0 g
Sodium: 452mg
Fat: 4 g

Peppered Mackerel Fillets

Preparation Time: 10 minutes
Cooking Time: 20 minutes
Servings: 2

Ingredients:

- 2 (7 oz.) mackerel fillets
- 1 tablespoon melted unsalted low-fat butter
- Salt & ground black pepper as needed

Directions:

1. Begin by preheating the oven to 350 degrees Fahrenheit and put a rack in the center.
2. Grease a baking dish, apply butter on the fillets, and season with salt and pepper.
3. Put the fillets in the prepared baking dish in a single layer to bake for 20 minutes.
4. Once cooked, serve immediately and enjoy!

Nutrition:

Calories: 189
Protein: 19 g
Fiber: 1 g
Carbohydrates: 1 g
Sugar: 1 g
Sodium: 246mg
Fat: 11 g

Tuna Patties

Preparation Time: 15 minutes
Cooking Time: 10 minutes
Servings: 2

Ingredients:

- 3 cups lettuce
- 1 tablespoon low-fat butter
- 1 whisked organic egg
- ½ chopped celery stalk
- 2 tablespoons low-fat mayonnaise
- 1 teaspoon chopped fresh dill
- 2 tablespoons chopped walnuts
- 2 tablespoons chopped fresh parsley
- 15 oz. can drained water-packed tuna

Directions:

1. Combine all the ingredients together except butter and lettuce in a bowl and mix thoroughly.
2. Make two equal-sized patties from the mixture.
3. Heat the butter in a pan and cook the patties for 3 minutes from both sides until done.
4. Serve with lettuce and enjoy!

Nutrition:

Calories: 116
Protein: 13 g
Fiber: 1 g
Carbohydrates: 9 g
Sugar: 1 g
Sodium: 2mg
Fat: 2 g

Fish Chowder

Preparation Time: 20 minutes
Cooking Time: 3 hours
Servings: 6

Ingredients:

- 1 cup milk
- 10 oz. water
- 14 oz. haddock
- 1 tablespoon salt
- 6 oz. chopped bacon
- 1 cup chopped potato
- 1 cup diced yellow onion
- 1 teaspoon ground thyme
- ½ teaspoon ground black pepper

Directions:

1. Put bacon in a skillet and roast for 2 minutes over high flame.
2. Once crunchy, put in the slow cooker.
3. Add the haddock to the slow cooker, too.
4. Add the rest of the ingredients and stir.
5. Cover and cook on high for 3 hours.
6. Stir in between with a wooden spoon.
7. Serve once done!

Nutrition:

Calories: 229
Protein: 22 g
Fiber: 6 g
Carbohydrates: 9 g
Sugar: 10 g
Sodium: 803mg
Fat: 11 g

Broiled Fish Fillets

Preparation Time: 5 minutes
Cooking Time: 5 minutes
Servings: 4

Ingredients:

- ½ teaspoon canola oil
- ½ teaspoon lemon juice
- Lemon wedges as needed
- 1 teaspoon grated lemon zest
- ⅛ teaspoon freshly ground pepper
- 2 tablespoons softened unsalted butter
- 4 (5 oz.) thin, white-fleshed fish fillets
- ¼ teaspoon & a pinch of kosher salt divided

Directions:

1. Begin by preheating the broiler and grease a medium-rimmed baking sheet with oil.
2. In the meantime, combine butter, lemon juice, zest, and the remaining salt in a small bowl.
3. Rub this mixture on the fish with ¼ teaspoon salt and pepper.
4. Put fish on the prepared baking sheet in a single layer.
5. Broil without turning for 8 minutes or until the fish flakes effortlessly with a fork.
6. Remove the fish once cooked to divide among 4 plates.
7. Serve with lemon wedges and enjoy.

Nutrition:

Calories: 170
Protein: 24 g
Fiber: 0 g
Carbohydrates: 0 g
Sugar: 0 g
Sodium: 250mg
Fat: 8 g

Herb Crust Grilled Salmon

Preparation Time: 10 minutes
Cooking Time: 30 minutes
Servings: 1

Ingredients:

- 1 garlic clove
- ⅓ cup cilantro
- ½ cup oregano
- ¼ teaspoon salt
- ¼ cup green onion
- 1 tablespoon olive oil
- 4 skinless salmon fillets
- 1 tablespoon lemon juice
- ¼ teaspoon black pepper

Directions:

1. Begin by preheating the oven to 400 degrees Fahrenheit and make a pocket for each fillet by using aluminum foil.
2. Chop the oregano, cilantro, onion, and garlic.
3. Put it in a blender along with olive oil, lemon juice, salt, and pepper, and blend until well combined.
4. Coat the salmon with this mixture and seal it in the pocket to bake for half an hour.
5. Once the salmon is cooked through, serve and enjoy!

Nutrition:

Calories: 237
Protein: 18 g
Fiber: 0 g
Carbohydrates: 3 g
Sugar: 0 g
Sodium: 362mg
Fat: 17 g

Grilled Black Cod

Preparation Time: 10 minutes
Cooking Time: 10 minutes
Servings: 4

Ingredients:

- 4 cod fillets
- 1 teaspoon pepper
- 1 teaspoon garlic powder
- 2 teaspoons chili powder
- 2 teaspoons cumin powder
- 2 teaspoons taco seasoning

Directions:

1. Combine all the ingredients except the fish in a bowl and marinate fillets with it.
2. Start heating the griddle at high heat and grease with cooking spray.
3. Cook the fish fillets on the hot griddle top for 5 minutes from both sides.
4. Remove to serve once cooked, and enjoy!

Nutrition:

Calories: 450
Protein: 21 g
Fiber: 0 g
Carbohydrates: 1 g
Sugar: 1 g
Sodium: 120mg
Fat: 40 g

Cajun Crab

Preparation Time: 10 minutes
Cooking Time: 10 minutes
Serving: 2

Ingredients:

- 2 bay leaves
- 1 teaspoon olive oil
- 1 fresh & quartered lemon
- 3 tablespoons Cajun seasoning
- 4 pre-cooked & defrosted snow crab legs

Directions:

1. Fill a large pot halfway with salt and water.
2. Let it come to a boil over high heat, squeeze in the lemon juice, and throw in the leftover quarter.
3. Stir in bay leaves and Cajun seasoning for a minute.
4. Boil the crab legs in this water for 8 minutes, making sure they're completely submerged the entire time.
5. Use olive oil as a dipping sauce for the legs.
6. Serve immediately and enjoy!

Nutrition:

Calories: 381
Protein: 83 g
Fiber: 1 g
Carbohydrates: 11 g
Sugar: 2 g
Sodium: 590mg
Fat: 3 g

Salmon & Kale

Preparation Time: 10 minutes
Cooking Time: 15 minutes
Servings: 4

Ingredients:

- 1 sliced lemon
- ½ teaspoon paprika
- 4 fresh thyme sprigs
- ¼ cup dry white wine
- 1 pound salmon fillets
- 2 sliced small zucchini
- 4 fresh rosemary sprigs
- 2 cups thinly sliced kale leaves
- Freshly ground black pepper as needed

Directions:

1. Begin by preheating the oven to 450 degrees Fahrenheit and cut 4 pieces of parchment paper, each almost 12 inches in diameter.
2. Put ½ cup kale leaves on each piece of paper, place several slices of zucchini on top, and sprinkle pepper.
3. Sprinkle paprika over salmon fillets and add a single thyme sprig, rosemary sprig, and a slice of lemon over each fillet.
4. Pour a tablespoon of white wine over each fillet.
5. Fold the parchment paper over to join the seams and crease to create a seal.
6. Set this in the oven to bake for 15 minutes.
7. Remove once done and cool for 5 minutes before serving.

Nutrition:

Calories: 357
Protein: 32 g
Fiber: 2 g
Carbohydrates: 11 g
Sugar: 2 g
Sodium: 340mg
Fat: 21 g

Salmon & Kalamata Olives

Preparation Time: 10 minutes
Cooking Time: 20 minutes
Servings: 3
Ingredients:

- 1 cup fish broth
- 1 teaspoon sea salt
- ½ teaspoon cumin
- ½ thinly sliced lemon
- 4 (0.3 lb.) salmon fillets
- ½ cup sliced red onion
- ½ cup essential olive oil
- ¼ teaspoon black pepper
- 1 can of pitted kalamata olives
- 1 teaspoon herbs de Provence
- 2 tablespoons fresh lemon juice

Directions:

1. Turn your instant pot on SAUTE mode and season salmon with cumin, salt, and pepper.
2. Heat olive oil in the pot and add the fish to brown from both sides.
3. Stir in the remaining ingredients and lock the lid to let it simmer on MANUAL HIGH for 10 minutes.
4. Release pressure steam quickly and serve!

Nutrition:

Calories: 440
Protein: 30 g
Fiber: 5 g
Carbohydrates: 3 g
Sugar: 5 g
Sodium: 889mg
Fat: 34 g

Flavored Octopus

Preparation Time: 10 minutes
Cooking Time: 8 minutes
Servings: 4
Ingredients:

- 0.6 pounds octopus
- 3 tablespoons lime juice
- Salt & pepper as needed
- 2 teaspoons garlic powder
- 1 teaspoon chopped cilantro
- 2 tablespoons extra virgin olive oil

Directions:

1. Add the octopus to the steaming basket and season with all the remaining ingredients.
2. Add water to the instant pot and lower the steaming basket.
3. Cook for 8 minutes on HIGH with the lid on.
4. Follow a simple pressure release and serve once done!

Nutrition:

Calories: 120
Protein: 30 g
Fiber: 5 g
Carbohydrates: 1 g
Sugar: 1 g
Sodium: 420mg
Fat: 3 g

Fish Stew

Preparation Time: 5 minutes
Cooking Time: 20 minutes
Servings: 3

Ingredients:

- 1 bay leaf
- ½ lb. shrimp
- ½ lb. mussels
- 100 g. halibut
- 1 cup light cream
- 2 cups chicken broth
- 2 crushed garlic cloves
- ½ cup coconut cream
- 1 dried whole star anise
- ½ teaspoon black pepper
- 3 tablespoons coconut oil
- 2 tablespoons lemon juice

Directions:

1. Sauté bay leaves in an instant pot in coconut oil with star anise for 30 seconds.
2. Stir in garlic and add broth to the pot.
3. Meanwhile, marinate the fish fillets with lemon juice, salt, and pepper.
4. Add them to the pot with shrimp and mussels, too.
5. Cook for 10 minutes and release pressure naturally.
6. Add in the creams and let it all simmer.
7. Discard the bay leaf and star anise before serving!

Nutrition:

Calories: 535
Protein: 27 g
Fiber: 3 g
Carbohydrates: 8 g
Sugar: 6 g
Sodium: 800mg
Fat: 44 g

CHAPTER 6:
VEGAN DIABETIC-FRIENDLY RECIPES

Zucchini Hummus

Preparation Time: 10 minutes
Cooking Time: 0 minutes
Servings: 5

Ingredients:

- 2 chopped zucchinis
- 1 teaspoon turmeric powder
- 1 teaspoon ground coriander
- 1 diced garlic clove
- 1 tablespoon tahini paste
- 3 tablespoons extra-virgin olive oil
- 1 teaspoon harissa

Directions:

1. Add all the ingredients to the blender.
2. Blend until smooth.
3. Cook it slightly in a pan.
4. Serve immediately!

Nutrition:

Calories: 107
Protein: 1 g
Fiber: 1 g
Carbohydrates: 3 g
Sugar: 2 g
Sodium: 124mg
Fat: 10 g

Spinach Chips

Preparation Time: 10 minutes
Cooking Time: 20 minutes
Servings: 4

Ingredients:

- 1 oz. washed & dried baby spinach
- 1 teaspoon sweet paprika
- Cooking spray
- Sea salt and black pepper to taste
- ½ teaspoon dried oregano

Directions:

1. Grease a baking sheet with cooking spray.
2. Spread baby spinach on it.
3. Add the remaining ingredients and bake at 435 degrees Fahrenheit for 20 minutes.
4. Once done, serve immediately!

Nutrition:

Calories: 140
Protein: 4 g
Fiber: 2 g
Carbohydrates: 6 g
Sugar: 0 g
Sodium: 130mg
Fat: 4 g

Avocado Salsa

Preparation Time: 10 minutes
Cooking Time: 0 minutes
Servings: 6

Ingredients:

- 3 cups chopped tomatoes
- 1 cup peeled, pitted & chopped avocado
- 1 tablespoon pitted & sliced black olives
- 2 teaspoons balsamic vinegar
- 1 tablespoon chopped basil
- A pinch of sea salt and black pepper
- 1 chopped onion
- 2 teaspoons capers
- 3 minced garlic cloves

Directions:

1. Add all the ingredients to a bowl and toss to combine.
2. Serve as an appetizer.

Nutrition:

Calories: 201
Protein: 6 g
Fiber: 3 g
Carbohydrates: 8 g
Sugar: 20 g
Sodium: 680mg
Fat: 10 g

Healthy Kale Bowls

Preparation Time: 10 minutes
Cooking Time: 10 minutes
Servings: 4

Ingredients:

- 2 tablespoons chopped almonds
- 2 tablespoons chopped walnuts
- 2 bunches of trimmed & chopped kale
- 1 cup halved cherry tomatoes
- 2 tablespoons avocado oil
- 1 lemon juice
- ⅔ cup charred roasted peppers
- 1 teaspoon Italian seasoning
- ¼ teaspoon chili powder
- Sea Salt & black pepper as needed

Directions:

1. Heat oil in a pan over medium heat.
2. Cook the kale for 5 minutes.
3. Add the remaining ingredients and stir properly.
4. Cook for 5 minutes more and divide into bowls.
5. Serve immediately!

Nutrition:

Calories: 143
Protein: 7 g
Fiber: 4 g
Carbohydrates: 9 g
Sugar: 0 g
Sodium: 0mg
Fat: 5 g

Healthy Veggie Sticks

Preparation Time: 10 minutes
Cooking Time: 15 minutes
Servings: 4

Ingredients:

- 1 cut into sticks red sweet pepper
- 2 cut into sticks celery stalks
- 1 peeled & cut into sticks carrot
- 1 tablespoon extra-virgin olive oil
- 1 freshly squeezed lemon juice
- A pinch of sea salt and black pepper

Directions:

1. Combine all the ingredients in a bowl.
2. Toss and spread onto a parchment paper-lined baking sheet.
3. Bake at 400 degrees Fahrenheit for 15 minutes.
4. Serve immediately!

Nutrition:

Calories: 22
Protein: 0 g
Fiber: 1 g
Carbohydrates: 4 g
Sugar: 6 g
Sodium: 440mg
Fat: 0 g

Vegetable Minestrone

Preparation Time: 15 minutes
Cooking Time: 25 minutes
Servings: 4

Ingredients:

- 3 minced garlic cloves
- 2 peeled & diced carrots
- 1 diced celery stalk
- 1 ½ tablespoons extra-virgin olive oil
- 1 diced onion
- ⅛ teaspoon freshly ground black pepper
- ¼ teaspoon dried thyme
- 7 cups low-sodium vegetable stock
- 2 bay leaves
- ¼ teaspoon red pepper flakes
- 4 oz. whole wheat pasta
- 4 cups fresh baby spinach
- ¼ cup freshly squeezed lemon juice
- 2 medium sliced zucchinis
- ¼ cup chopped fresh parsley

Directions:

1. Take a stockpot and heat the oil.
2. Add onion, garlic, celery, and carrots, and cook until onion becomes tender.
3. Next, add black pepper, thyme, bay leaf, and chili flakes, and cook for a minute until you start smelling the aroma.
4. Pour in the vegetable stock, stir, and boil.
5. Add pasta, reduce heat to a simmer, and cook for 12 minutes or until al dente.
6. Next, put in zucchini and cook for another 2 minutes.
7. Lastly, stir in the spinach and lemon juice for 2 minutes.
8. Top with parsley and serve in bowls.

Nutrition:

Calories: 217
Protein: 5 g
Fiber: 5 g
Carbohydrates: 36 g
Sugar: 4 g
Sodium: 766mg
Fat: 6 g

Vegan Brown Rice Burgers

Preparation Time: 10 minutes
Cooking Time: 5 minutes
Servings 12

Ingredients:

- 1 cup grated carrot
- ½ cup chopped onion
- ¼ teaspoon ground black pepper
- Flax egg to combine
- 1 minced garlic clove
- 2 cups cooked brown rice
- ½ cup parsley
- 1 teaspoon sea salt
- ½ cup whole wheat flour
- 2 tablespoons vegetable oil

Directions:

1. Mix all the ingredients except oil in a bowl.
2. Make 12 patties out of the mixture.
3. Drizzle vegetable oil over a frying pan and heat over medium flame.
4. Cook patties on the pan until golden brown.
5. Flip them to cook properly.
6. Serve hot!

Nutrition:

Calories: 120
Protein: 3 g
Fiber: 3 g
Carbohydrates: 18 g
Sugar: 4 g
Sodium: 150mg
Fat: 3 g

Easy Quinoa Bowl

Preparation Time: 15 minutes
Cooking Time: 15 minutes
Servings: 4

Ingredients:

- 2 cups water
- 1 cup diced tomatoes
- 1 cup diced sweet pepper
- ½ teaspoon grated lemon zest
- 1 tablespoon extra-virgin olive oil
- 1 cup quinoa
- ½ cup cooked brown rice
- 1 tablespoon lemon juice

Directions:

1. Add water and quinoa to a pan and cook for 15 minutes.
2. Once tender, remove it from heat and set aside to cool for 10 minutes.
3. Mix sweet pepper, tomatoes, lemon juice, zest, rice, and olive oil in a large bowl.
4. Add quinoa next and mix to combine.
5. Transfer the mixture into bowls and serve immediately.

Nutrition:

Calories: 290
Protein: 8 g
Fiber: 4 g
Carbohydrates: 49 g
Sugar: 2 g
Sodium: 11mg
Fat: 6 g

Ginger Congee

Preparation Time: 10 minutes
Cooking Time: 1 hour
Servings: 1

Ingredients:

- 1 cup brown rice
- Sesame seed oil for garnish
- Sliced green onion for topping
- 1 inch peeled & thinly sliced ginger
- 7 cups low-sodium vegetable stock
- Sea salt as needed

Directions:

1. Add rice, ginger, stock, and salt to a pot.
2. Bring to a boil, stir, and reduce to a simmer for an hour.
3. It should be creamy and thick once done.
4. Dish out on a plate, top with green onion, and drizzle some sesame seed oil to serve.

Nutrition:

Calories: 510
Protein: 13 g
Fiber: 6 g
Carbohydrates: 60 g
Sugar: 2 g
Sodium: 840mg
Fat: 24 g

Healthy Potato Casserole

Preparation Time: 10 minutes
Cooking Time: 15 minutes
Servings: 2

Ingredients:

- ¼ teaspoon black pepper
- 2 tablespoons extra-virgin olive oil
- ½ cup chopped green onions
- 16 fresh potatoes
- 1 teaspoon dried dill weed
- Water as needed

Directions:

1. Boil potatoes in water in a pan over medium heat until tender.
2. Drain the water and let it cool for 20 minutes.
3. Mix olive oil, dill, and black pepper in a bowl.
4. Cut the potatoes into small pieces and toss them in the mixture to coat.
5. Put in the fridge to chill and enjoy once set.

Nutrition:

Calories: 237
Protein: 5 g
Fiber: 6 g
Carbohydrates: 46 g
Sugar: 7 g
Sodium: 22mg
Fat: 3

Parmesan Roasted Broccoli

Preparation Time: 10 minutes
Cooking Time: 10 minutes
Servings: 4

Ingredients:

- 1 minced fresh garlic
- Kosher salt as needed
- 3 tablespoons olive oil
- ½ teaspoon lemon zest
- 1 oz. grated parmesan cheese fresh
- Freshly ground black pepper as needed
- 4 cups washed & well-drained broccoli florets

Directions:

1. Start by preheating the oven to 450 degrees Fahrenheit.
2. Combine all the ingredients except cheese in a bowl and toss to coat.
3. Line a baking dish with foil and grease with cooking spray.
4. Evenly spread the broccoli mixture and put it in the oven to roast for 10 minutes or until crispy.
5. Serve once done, and enjoy with cheese on top!

Nutrition:

Calories: 163
Protein: 6 g
Fiber: 3 g
Carbohydrates: 8 g
Sugar: 2 g
Sodium: 146mg
Fat: 13

Gnocchi With Zucchini Ribbons

Preparation Time: 10 minutes
Cooking Time: 10 minutes
Servings: 4

Ingredients:

- 2 tablespoons low-fat butter
- ½ teaspoon kosher salt
- 1 lb fresh/frozen gnocchi
- ¼ teaspoon grated nutmeg
- 2 chopped medium shallots
- ½ cup chopped fresh parsley
- 1 halved pint of cherry tomatoes
- ½ cup grated parmesan cheese
- Freshly ground pepper as needed
- 3 finely-sliced-lengthwise small zucchini

Directions:

1. Boil water in a large saucepan over medium heat.
2. Cook the gnocchi in it for 5 minutes according to the package instructions.
3. Remove from heat and drain the water.
4. Meanwhile, melt butter in a skillet over medium-high heat until it turns brown.
5. Stir in zucchini and shallots to cook in the butter for 3 minutes.
6. Stir in tomatoes, nutmeg, salt, and pepper to cook for 2 minutes.
7. Once the tomatoes start to mush, stir in parsley, parmesan, and gnocchi.
8. Toss well until coated, and serve once done!

Nutrition:

Calories: 426
Protein: 17 g
Fiber: 4 g
Carbohydrates: 66 g
Sugar: 7 g
Sodium: 752mg
Fat: 11

Thai-Style Eggplant Dip

Preparation Time: 10 minutes
Cooking Time: 30 minutes
Servings: 4

Ingredients:

- 2 garlic cloves
- 1 jalapeño pepper
- 2 teaspoons sugar
- ¼ cup chopped basil
- 1 pound Thai eggplant
- 2 tablespoons rice vinegar
- 1 teaspoon low-sodium soy sauce
- Cut vegetables/crackers for serving

Directions:

1. Start by preheating the oven to 425 degrees Fahrenheit and use a skewer or knife to pierce an eggplant in several places.
2. Put it on a rimmed baking tray to bake for half an hour until soft.
3. Allow it to cool, slice it in half, scoop the flesh of the eggplant, and transfer it to a blender.
4. Add in sugar, soy sauce, rice vinegar, basil, garlic, and jalapeno, and blend until smooth.
5. Serve with cut vegetables or crackers, and enjoy!

Nutrition:

Calories: 557
Protein: 17 g
Fiber: 2 g
Carbohydrates: 39 g
Sugar: 2 g
Sodium: 160mg
Fat: 36

Roasted Root Vegetables

Preparation Time: 10 minutes
Cooking Time: 25 minutes
Servings: 6

Ingredients:

- 1 cup chopped turnips
- 1 cup chopped parsnips
- 1 cup chopped rutabaga
- 1 tablespoon extra-virgin olive oil
- 1 teaspoon fresh chopped rosemary
- Freshly ground black pepper as needed

Directions:

1. Start by preheating the oven to 400 degrees Fahrenheit.
2. Combine all the ingredients in a bowl and place on the baking sheet without overlapping.
3. Bake until the vegetables are browned and soft, flipping halfway once for even cooking.
4. Serve immediately and enjoy!

Nutrition:

Calories: 112
Protein: 1 g
Fiber: 3 g
Carbohydrates: 15 g
Sugar: 6 g
Sodium: 203mg
Fat: 5

Roasted Mint Carrots

Preparation Time: 5 minutes
Cooking Time: 20 minutes
Servings: 6

Ingredients:

- 1-pound trimmed carrots
- ¼ cup thinly sliced mint
- 1 tablespoon extra-virgin olive oil
- Freshly ground black pepper as needed

Directions:

1. Start by preheating the oven at 425 degrees Fahrenheit.
2. Place the carrots in a rimmed baking tray without overlapping.
3. Drizzle olive oil, coat the carrots on the sheet by shaking them carefully, and sprinkle pepper over them.
4. Roast until browned and tender, flipping twice halfway for even cooking.
5. Sprinkle mint on top and serve immediately!

Nutrition:

Calories: 182
Protein: 1 g
Fiber: 3 g
Carbohydrates: 14 g
Sugar: 8 g
Sodium: 240mg
Fat: 14

CHAPTER 7:
FRESH & FLAVORFUL SALADS

Red Bean Salad

Preparation Time: 5 minutes
Cooking Time: 0 minutes
Servings: 2

Ingredients:

- ¼ cup olive oil
- ⅔ teaspoon salt
- 1 chopped cucumber
- ½ cup diced red onion
- 1 can of drained red beans
- 1 drained can of chickpeas
- ¼ cup red wine vinegar
- 1 can of drained green beans
- 1 tablespoon chopped parsley
- 1 can of drained cannellini beans
- ⅓ teaspoon ground black pepper

Directions:

1. Mix all the ingredients together in a bowl and toss to coat.
2. Serve right away and enjoy!

Nutrition:

Calories: 204
Fat: 2 g
Sodium: 462mg
Fiber: 8 g
Protein: 7 g
Carbohydrates: 42 g
Sugars: 22 g

Ambrosia Fruit Salad

Preparation Time: 5 minutes
Cooking Time: 0 minutes
Servings: 1

Ingredients:

- 1 cup green grapes
- ¾ cup low-fat yogurt
- 1 peeled & sliced banana
- 1 cup seedless red grapes
- 1 cup miniature marshmallows
- 1 can of drained fruit cocktail
- ½ sweetened cup shredded coconut
- 8 oz. can unsweetened & drained pineapple chunks

Directions:

1. Mix all the ingredients in a bowl until well combined.
2. Refrigerate to chill before serving!

Nutrition:

Calories: 290
Fat: 14 g
Sodium: 45mg
Fiber: 4 g
Protein: 2 g
Carbohydrates: 43 g
Sugars: 36 g

Artichoke Salad

Preparation Time: 30 minutes
Cooking Time: 10 minutes
Servings: 6

Ingredients:

- 1 ½ lemon juice
- 1 minced shallot
- 1 teaspoon Dijon mustard
- 1/2 cup minced red onion
- 6 drained tablespoons capers
- Extra virgin olive oil as needed
- 2 teaspoons divided kosher salt
- ½ cup chopped fresh basil leaves
- 2 thinly sliced roasted red peppers
- ½ cup chopped fresh parsley leaves
- 9 oz. frozen artichoke hearts, defrosted boxes
- 4 tablespoons divided white wine vinegar
- 1 teaspoon divided freshly ground black pepper

Directions:

1. Start by preheating the air fryer at 390 degrees Fahrenheit.
2. Mix artichoke hearts with half a teaspoon of pepper and 1 teaspoon of salt in a bowl.
3. Pour in olive oil and shake to coat well.
4. Grease the air fryer basket with olive oil and add the coated artichokes without overcrowding.
5. Cook for 5 minutes from both sides.
6. Now, add 1 tablespoon vinegar, mustard, shallot, lemon juice, half a teaspoon of pepper, and 1 teaspoon salt to a food processor and pulse.
7. Add basil leaves and slowly add olive oil to the mixture while processing until smooth like a paste.
8. Remove artichoke hearts to a serving bowl once cooked and combine with the vinaigrette.
9. Combine with the remaining vinegar and ingredients.
10. Toss carefully to combine and set aside for half an hour before serving!

Nutrition:
Calories: 348
Fat: 28 g
Sodium: 149mg
Fiber: 4 g
Protein: 5 g
Carbohydrates: 17 g
Sugars: 0 g

Salmon & Bean Salad

Preparation Time: 5 minutes
Cooking Time: 0 minutes
Servings: 1

Ingredients:

- ¼ teaspoon salt
- 1 teaspoon honey
- 2 oz. baby spinach
- ⅛ dried chili flakes
- ½ cup rapeseed oil
- 1 can of drained sweetcorn
- ¼ cup white wine vinegar
- 1 can of drained haricot beans
- ½ diced medium cucumber
- 10 quartered cherry tomatoes
- ¼ teaspoon ground black pepper
- 1 pouch ready-to-cook couscous
- 1 can pack in water-drained pink salmon

Directions:

1. Add together salt, chili flakes, honey, vinegar, rapeseed oil, and pepper in a jar and close the lid to shake until well combined.
2. Combine the remaining ingredients in a bowl and drizzle the jar dressing over it.
3. Toss to coat and serve as a salad.

Nutrition:
Calories: 346
Fat: 13 g
Sodium: 317mg
Fiber: 11 g
Protein: 27 g
Carbohydrates: 26 g
Sugars: 4 g

Berry Avocado salad

Preparation Time: 5 minutes
Cooking Time: 0 minutes
Servings: 1

Ingredients:

- ¼ cup pecans
- Salt as needed
- ¼ cup blackberries
- ¼ cup cherry tomatoes
- Lemon juice as needed
- ½ cup pomegranate seeds
- Olive oil/avocado oil as needed
- 1 cut-into-½-inch pieces ripe avocado
- 1 cup mixed greens (spinach, arugula, red leaf lettuce)

Directions:

1. Combine all the ingredients except olive oil, lemon juice, and salt.
2. Whisk the exceptions in a bowl and pour over the salad.
3. Toss to coat and serve once done!

Nutrition:

Calories: 285
Fat: 22 g
Sodium: 86mg
Fiber: 5 g
Protein: 6 g
Carbohydrates: 19 g
Sugars: 9 g

Cherry Tuna Salad

Preparation Time: 5 minutes
Cooking Time: 0 minutes
Servings: 3

Ingredients:

- ¼ cup baby rocket leaves
- 1 ⅓ cups cooked brown rice
- 2 chopped medium cucumbers
- 7 oz. quartered cherry tomatoes
- ½ cup fat-free balsamic dressing
- 15 oz. drained & flaked can pack in water tuna

Directions:

1. Put cooked rice in a bowl and drizzle balsamic dressing; toss to mix.
2. Let rice sit for 15 minutes, and then add in the remaining ingredients and toss to combine.
3. Adjust the seasoning to taste and serve your salad!

Nutrition:

Calories: 187
Fat: 22 g
Sodium: 402mg
Fiber: 0 g
Protein: 16 g
Carbohydrates: 9 g
Sugars: 0 g

Greek Chicken Salad

Preparation Time: 14 minutes
Cooking Time: 0 minutes
Servings: 2

Ingredients:

- 2 cups sliced tomatoes
- ¼ cup kalamata olives
- 1 cup sliced cucumber
- 6 cups chopped romaine lettuce
- ¼ cup broken-into-chunks feta cheese
- 1 (8 oz.) finely chopped Greek marinated chicken breast

(Greek Dressing)

- 1 teaspoon sugar
- 2 teaspoon oregano
- ¼ cup red wine vinegar
- ¼ cup extra virgin olive oil
- 1 peeled & minced garlic clove
- ½ teaspoon each of kosher salt
- ½ freshly ground black pepper

Directions:

1. Divide lettuce among two bowls and mix in with the remaining ingredients except the dressing.
2. Combine all the dressing ingredients together in a jar, close the lid, and shake to mix.
3. Put the dressing over the salad and toss.
4. Serve once done, and enjoy!

Nutrition:

Calories: 334
Fat: 25 g
Sodium: 476mg
Fiber: 1 g
Protein: 3 g
Carbohydrates: 5 g
Sugars: 3 g

Easy Broccoli Salad

Preparation Time: 5 minutes
Cooking Time: 0 minutes
Servings: 4

Ingredients:

- ½ red chili
- 1 broccoli head
- 2 handfuls nuts
- 1 tablespoon low-fat butter/olive oil
- 2 tablespoons heaped pomegranate seeds

Directions:

1. Steam the broccoli until tender and place in a serving dish along with the remaining ingredients.
2. Toss to combine well and enjoy the salad!

Nutrition:

Calories: 196
Fat: 13 g
Sodium: 214mg
Fiber: 0 g
Protein: 6 g
Carbohydrates: 16 g
Sugars: 9 g

Walnut & Berry Salad

Preparation Time: 10 minutes
Cooking Time 0 minutes
Servings: 4

Ingredients:

- 1 teaspoon honey
- 4 cups spring mix
- ¼ teaspoon kosher salt
- ½ cup fresh blueberries
- 1 oz. softened goat cheese
- 1 cup quartered strawberries
- 3 tablespoons whole buttermilk
- 2 tablespoons toasted chopped walnuts
- ⅛ teaspoon freshly ground black pepper

Directions:

1. Combine all the ingredients in a bowl and mix well.
2. Serve once done, and enjoy!

Nutrition:

Calories: 91
Fat: 1 g
Sodium: 114mg
Fiber: 6 g
Protein: 4 g
Carbohydrates: 10 g
Sugars: 9 g

Spinach & Orange Salad

Preparation Time: 5 minutes
Cooking Time: 0 minutes
Servings: 4

Ingredients:

- 6 oz. baby spinach
- 1 mandarin orange juice & zest
- 1 tablespoon extra-virgin olive oil
- Freshly ground black pepper as needed
- 2 peeled & membranes-removed mandarin oranges

Directions:

1. Toss and combine all the ingredients in a bowl.
2. Serve immediately and enjoy!

Nutrition:

Calories: 221
Fat: 18 g
Sodium: 474mg
Fiber: 3 g
Protein: 2 g
Carbohydrates: 14 g
Sugars: 15 g

Greek Avocado Salad

Preparation Time: 20 minutes
Cooking Time: 0 minutes
Servings: 8
Ingredients:

- 2 teaspoon sugar
- 1 tablespoon oregano
- 1 teaspoon kosher salt
- ½ cup red wine vinegar
- ½ cup extra virgin olive oil
- ¼ small thinly sliced red onion
- ¼ cup chopped Italian flat leaf
- 2 peeled & minced garlic cloves
- 2 avocados pitted & cut-into-chunks
- 1 cup broken-into-chunks feta cheese
- 1 ½ cups pitted & halved kalamata olives
- 1 teaspoon freshly ground black pepper
- 1 ½ pounds stemmed & quartered medium tomatoes
- 2 peeled-in-stripes & cut-into-½-inch-slices cucumbers

Directions:

1. Combine olive oil, garlic, sugar, vinegar, salt, oregano, and pepper in a jar, close the lid, shake, and set aside.
2. Combine the remaining ingredients in a bowl and add the dressing.
3. Toss, serve, and enjoy!

Nutrition:
Calories: 323
Fat: 22 g
Sodium: 614mg
Fiber: 6 g
Protein: 5 g
Carbohydrates: 14 g
Sugars: 6 g

Quinoa Apple Salad

Preparation Time: 5 minutes
Cooking Time: 0 minutes
Servings: 8
Ingredients:

- 1 chopped large apple
- Kosher salt as needed
- 3 tablespoons lemon juice
- ¾ cup crumbled feta cheese
- 2 cups cooked & cooled quinoa
- 2 tablespoons extra-virgin olive oil
- 2 cups roughly chopped shredded kale
- Freshly ground black pepper as needed
- ½ cup coarsely chopped whole raw almonds

Directions:

1. Combine all the ingredients and drizzle lemon juice and oil in the last.
2. Toss, combine well, and serve cold or warm as you like.

Nutrition:
Calories: 235
Fat: 15 g
Sodium: 180mg
Fiber: 4 g
Protein: 6 g
Carbohydrates: 11 g
Sugars: 9 g

Arugula Fruit Salad

Preparation Time: 20 minutes
Cooking Time: 0 minutes
Servings: 4

Ingredients:

- 8 cups arugula
- 1 teaspoon honey
- ¼ cup sliced almonds
- ¼ teaspoon kosher salt
- ¼ thinly sliced red onion
- 3 cups sliced strawberries
- ⅓ cup extra-virgin olive oil
- ½ cup crumbled feta cheese
- ¼ freshly ground black pepper
- 1 ½ tablespoons balsamic vinegar
- 3 cups chopped-into-½-inch-pieces seedless watermelon

Directions:

1. Combine vinegar, oil, salt, honey, and pepper in a bowl and whisk to mix well.
2. Combine the remaining ingredients in a bowl, add the dressing in as much as you like, and store the leftovers in the refrigerator for four days only.
3. Toss, serve, and enjoy!

Nutrition:

Calories: 338
Fat: 26 g
Sodium: 224mg
Fiber: 4 g
Protein: 5 g
Carbohydrates: 23 g
Sugars: 16 g

Celery & Arugula Salad

Preparation Time: 10 minutes
Cooking Time: 0 minutes
Servings: 4

Ingredients:

- 1 thinly sliced shallot
- 2 cups loosely packed arugula
- 1 tablespoon extra-virgin olive oil
- 2 tablespoons white wine vinegar
- 2 tablespoons grated Parmesan cheese
- Freshly ground black pepper as needed
- 3-cut-into-1-inch-pieces-of-¼-inch-thickness celery stalks

Directions:

1. Toss and combine all the ingredients in a bowl and top with cheese.
2. Serve immediately and enjoy!

Nutrition:

Calories: 160
Fat: 14 g
Sodium: 360mg
Fiber: 7 g
Protein: 3 g
Carbohydrates: 7 g
Sugars: 2 g

Cucumber Jicama Salad

Preparation Time: 15 minutes
Cooking Time: o minutes
Servings: 4

Ingredients:

- 1 lemon zest
- ½ lemon juice
- 12 oz. quartered white cherry tomatoes
- ¼ peeled & cut-into-matchsticks jicama
- 1 peeled & cut-into-thin-round-pieces large cucumber

Directions:

1. Combine all the ingredients in a bowl and mix well.
2. Serve once done, and enjoy!

Nutrition:

Calories: 46
Fat: 1 g
Sodium: 11mg
Fiber: 4 g
Protein: 2 g
Carbohydrates: 11 g
Sugars: 2 g

CHAPTER 8:
LOW-CARB COMFORT FOODS

Greek Chicken Drumettes

Preparation Time: 10 minutes
Cooking Time: 40 minutes
Servings: 8
Ingredients:
- 12 chicken wings
- 1 teaspoon oregano
- 2 tablespoons honey
- 1 minced garlic clove
- 2 tablespoons olive oil
- 3 tablespoons lemon juice

Directions:
1. Place the wings separately into sections and remove the wing tips.
2. Combine all the ingredients, leaving wings in a large plastic resealable bag.
3. Put the wings in the bag and seal.
4. Shake to coat and refrigerate the marinade for 8 hours or leave overnight.
5. Next, drain the chicken and put it in a baking pan.
6. Put the wings in the oven to bake at 400 degrees Fahrenheit (200°C, gas mark 6) for 30-40 minutes, until the chicken is tender and golden brown.
7. Serve once done, and enjoy with your favorite dip.

Nutrition:
Calories: 87
Fat: 5 g
Sodium: 64mg
Fiber: 0 g
Protein: 6 g
Carbohydrates: 5 g
Sugars: 4 g

Tomato Macaroni

Preparation Time: 10 minutes
Cooking Time: 15 minutes
Servings: 1
Ingredients:
- 8 oz. tomato paste
- ½ teaspoon honey
- 14 oz. diced tomatoes
- 8 oz. elbow macaroni
- 1 chopped small onion
- Salt & pepper as needed
- 2 tablespoons low-fat butter

Directions:
1. Follow the package instructions to cook the macaroni al dente and drain.
2. Add a tablespoon of butter to the macaroni and combine well to melt the butter.
3. Melt the remaining butter in a skillet over medium heat and sauté onions until tender.
4. Mix in paste and honey and allow it to simmer for 5 minutes.
5. Transfer the tomatoes and macaroni to the skillet and sprinkle salt and pepper over it.
6. Thoroughly combine to coat and let it simmer over low heat uncovered for 15 minutes.
7. Once cooked, serve and enjoy!

Nutrition:
Calories: 154
Fat: 4 g
Sodium: 362mg
Fiber: 2 g
Protein: 6 g
Carbohydrates: 26 g
Sugars: 5 g

Potato Barley Soup

Preparation Time: 20 minutes
Cooking Time: 40 minutes
Servings: 6

Ingredients:

- ¼ cup barley
- 2 diced tomatoes
- 2 ½ cups of water
- 1 teaspoon sea salt
- 1 cup chopped celery
- 1 cup chopped onions
- 1 cup chopped carrots
- 1 0.75 oz. vegetable broth
- 2 teaspoons minced garlic
- 14.5 oz. Peeled & diced potatoes
- ⅛ teaspoon ground black pepper
- 2 tablespoons extra-virgin olive oil

Directions:

1. Put a saucepan over medium flame to heat olive oil.
2. Stir in onions, garlic, carrots, and celery with a wooden spoon and cook until tender.
3. Add the leftover ingredients and let it come to a boil.
4. Bring the heat to a simmer for 40 minutes.
5. Serve immediately and enjoy!

Nutrition:

Calories: 143
Fat: 67 g
Sodium: 900mg
Fiber: 4 g
Protein: 8 g
Carbohydrates: 29 g
Sugars: 0 g

Air Fried Onion Rings

Preparation Time: 10 minutes
Cooking Time: 14 minutes
Servings: 5

Ingredients:

- 1 beaten egg
- ⅓ cup breadcrumbs
- 1 tablespoon sour cream
- 1 trimmed & sliced large white onion

Directions:

1. Turn the onion slices into onion rings by separating them with your hands.
2. Combine the sour cream and egg well.
3. Coat the onion rings with the wet mixture.
4. Next, dip them in the breadcrumbs and place them in the air fryer basket.
5. Shut the lid and air fry for 14 minutes at 395 degrees Fahrenheit.
6. Once crispy and golden, remove to a plate and serve hot.

Nutrition:

Calories: 58
Fat: 3 g
Sodium: 881mg
Fiber: 3 g
Protein: 11 g
Carbohydrates: 8 g
Sugars: 8 g

Healthy Carrot Soup

Preparation Time: 10 minutes
Cooking Time: 45 minutes
Servings: 4

Ingredients:

- 1 quarter broth
- 6 tablespoons olive oil
- Salt & pepper as needed
- Cayenne pepper as needed
- 8 washed & peeled large carrots

Directions:

1. Start by preheating the oven at 425 degrees Fahrenheit and place the carrots on a baking sheet.
2. Cover with olive oil and bake the carrots for 45 minutes or until tender.
3. Transfer the cooked carrots to a blender with the broth and blend to a puree.
4. Add the puree to a saucepan and heat it.
5. Sprinkle the cayenne, salt, and pepper.
6. Sprinkle some olive oil, stir, and serve immediately!

Nutrition:

Calories: 98
Fat: 4 g
Sodium: 784mg
Fiber: 3 g
Protein: 1 g
Carbohydrates: 16 g
Sugars: 8 g

Gluten-Free Stuffed Potatoes

Preparation Time: 15 minutes
Cooking Time: 15 minutes
Servings: 4

Ingredients:

- 2 (1 ½ pounds) medium sweet potatoes
- 2 cooked & chopped bacon slices divided
- 3 sliced scallions, divided
- ½ cup extra-sharp Cheddar cheese, shredded
- 4 tablespoons low-fat sour cream
- ¼ teaspoon salt
- ¼ teaspoon ground pepper

Directions:

1. Start by preheating the oven to 400 degrees F.
2. Use a fork to prick the sweet potatoes from all sides.
3. Put it in the microwave to cook for 12 minutes until soft on High.
4. Let it cool, and then slice the potatoes in half lengthwise.
5. Spoon out the potato flesh onto a medium bowl, making sure the potato shells remain intact.
6. Then mix cheese, a tablespoon of scallion, half bacon, salt, and pepper in the flesh.
7. Meanwhile, arrange the potato shells on a rimmed baking sheet.
8. Fill the potato shells equally with the potato mixture using a spoon.
9. Bake for 12-15 minutes until the cheese has melted and the potatoes appear nicely golden brown.
10. Remove them onto serving plates and cover each with a tablespoon of sour cream.
11. Garnish with the remaining scallion and bacon on top to serve!

Nutrition:

Calories: 148
Fat: 8 g
Sodium: 338mg
Fiber: 2 g
Protein: 6 g
Carbohydrates: 14 g
Sugars: 4 g

Mediterranean Lunch

Preparation Time: 5 minutes
Cooking Time: 0 minutes
Servings: 1

Ingredients:

- ¼ large sliced red bell pepper
- ¼ cup hummus
- ¼ teaspoon chopped fresh dill
- 2 tablespoons mixed olives
- 1 Persian cucumber/½ English cucumber, cut into spears
- ½ whole wheat 4-wedgie-cut pita bread

Directions:

1. Use a 4-cup divided sealable lunch box or container.
2. Put bell peppers, hummus, cucumber, pita, and olives in them.
3. If you prefer, keep the hummus and olives at the side in a small foil cup before using.
4. Sprinkle dill on cucumber and refrigerate this until serving.

Nutrition:

Calories: 194
Fat: 9 g
Sodium: 443mg
Fiber: 7 g
Protein: 8 g
Carbohydrates: 23 g
Sugars: 4 g

Italian Mushroom Soup

Preparation Time: 10 minutes
Cooking Time: 15 minutes
Servings: 3

Ingredients:

- 3 cups water
- 1 chopped onion
- Sea salt as needed
- Black pepper as needed
- 1 chopped red bell pepper
- ½ teaspoon minced garlic
- 1 teaspoon Italian herb mix
- 3 tablespoons low-fat butter
- 2 tablespoons almond flour
- 1 tablespoon chopped fresh chives
- 3 cups chopped cremini mushrooms

Directions:

1. Put a pot over medium flame to melt the butter.
2. Stir in onion and pepper with a wooden spoon for three minutes until translucent.
3. Stir in cremini mushrooms and garlic and cook until tender.
4. Sprinkle almond flour over the mushrooms and cook for a minute.
5. Add the leftover ingredients and let the water simmer until it thickens.
6. Serve in soup bowls garnished with fresh chives.

Nutrition:

Calories: 155
Fat: 7 g
Sodium: 462mg
Fiber: 1 g
Protein: 7 g
Carbohydrates: 18 g
Sugars: 5 g

Soy Pasta Soup

Preparation Time: 5 minutes
Cooking Time: 20 minutes
Servings: 4

Ingredients:

- 2 cups water
- 2 cups soy curls
- 1 cup frozen carrots
- 4 cups vegetable broth
- ¼ cup nutritional yeast
- 2 cups whole-grain pasta
- 1 cup frozen white onions
- 1 teaspoon dried rosemary
- ½ teaspoon ground black pepper

Directions:

1. Take a large saucepan, add all the ingredients, and boil over high heat.
2. Lower the flame to a simmer for 15 minutes or until the pasta is softened.
3. Ladle it out into soup bowls and serve immediately!

Nutrition:

Calories: 99
Fat: 1 g
Sodium: 434mg
Fiber: 6 g
Protein: 7 g
Carbohydrates: 13 g
Sugars: 0 g

Ginger Chicken

Preparation Time: 15 minutes
Cooking Time: 1 hour 15 minutes
Servings: 6

Ingredients:

- 2 garlic cloves
- 1 whole chicken
- 1 cup fresh cilantro leaves
- ¼ cup chopped fresh ginger
- 1 seeded & chopped jalapeño
- 2 tablespoons thinly sliced scallions
- 2 tablespoons low-sodium soy sauce

Directions:

1. Preheat the oven to 400 degrees Fahrenheit.
2. Pulse cilantro, jalapeno, ginger, garlic, scallions, and soy sauce in a food processor until finely minced.
3. Remove the neck and giblets from the cavity of the chicken.
4. Use fingers to loosen the skin from the breasts and drumsticks and carefully separate the skin from the chicken.
5. Rub the chicken and breast with the cilantro mix thoroughly.
6. Put the chicken in a large roasting pan and bake for an hour and 15 minutes, or until the thermometer inside the chicken thigh alerts 165°F.
7. Put the chicken on a platter, cover with foil loosely, and allow it to cool for 10 minutes.
8. Carve the chicken, divide accordingly, and remove the skin before eating.

Nutrition:

Calories: 149
Fat: 3 g
Sodium: 434mg
Fiber: 0 g
Protein: 26 g
Carbohydrates: 2 g
Sugars: 0 g

Orange Baked Chicken

Preparation Time: 10 minutes
Cooking Time: 15 minutes
Servings: 4

Ingredients:

- ¾ cup orange juice
- ½ teaspoon sesame oil
- ¼ cup thinly sliced scallions
- ⅛ teaspoon freshly ground pepper
- 2 teaspoons extra virgin olive oil
- 2 tablespoons low-sodium soy sauce
- 4 (6 oz.) bone-in & skin-on chicken breasts

Directions:

1. Preheat the oven to 375 degrees Fahrenheit.
2. Loosen the skin from the breasts without detaching gently.
3. Rub the underneath skin of the breasts with pepper.
4. Heat the oil in a large oven-proof skillet over medium-high heat.
5. Arrange the chicken breast skin side down and cook for 6 minutes from both sides until cooked, flipping once.
6. Combine orange juice, sesame oil, and soy sauce, and add the mix over the chicken.
7. Transfer the skillet to the oven and bake for half an hour until the chicken juice runs clear.
8. Divide among plates once done, garnish with scallions, and remove the skin from the chicken before eating.

Nutrition:

Calories: 200
Fat: 6 g
Sodium: 770mg
Fiber: 0 g
Protein: 28 g
Carbohydrates: 7 g
Sugars: 0 g

Turkey Vegetable Sauté

Preparation Time: 10 minutes
Cooking Time: 15 minutes
Servings: 6

Ingredients:

- 1 cup sliced carrot
- ½ cup sliced celery
- 4 oz. sliced mushrooms
- ½ teaspoon cumin
- ½ teaspoon garlic salt
- 1 cup chopped tomato
- 15 halved black olives
- 1 pound ground turkey
- 1 cup onion, cut into rings
- ½ cup chunked green bell pepper

Directions:

1. Cook the turkey until browned in a large skillet over medium heat.
2. Add in carrot, onion, celery, mushrooms, and bell pepper, and mix.
3. Saute in garlic, salt, and garlic, and cook until the vegetables are tender.
4. Stir in olives and tomato, and cook until everything is tender.
5. Serve once done, and enjoy!

Nutrition:

Calories: 197
Fat: 7 g
Sodium: 548mg
Fiber: 2 g
Protein: 25 g
Carbohydrates: 8 g
Sugars: 3 g

Borscht

Preparation Time: 10 minutes
Cooking Time: 15 minutes
Servings: 6
Ingredients:

- 16 oz. can beets
- 1 teaspoon sugar
- ½ cup chopped onion
- 2 teaspoons caraway seeds
- 3 tablespoons lemon juice
- 3 tablespoons unsalted butter
- 2 cups finely shredded cabbage
- 3 cups low-sodium chicken broth

Directions:

1. Place cabbage for 10 minutes in a pot of boiling water.
2. Remove the cabbage, save the water, and put it aside.
3. Add the onion in the same pot and sauté for a few minutes without browning.
4. Pour the chicken broth into the onion, cabbage, and the saved cabbage water.
5. Chop the beets and add them to the pot along with butter, caraway seeds, and beet juice.
6. Bring it to a simmer for 10 minutes and stir in lemon juice.
7. Serve with sour cream, and enjoy hot!

Nutrition:
Calories: 113
Fat: 7 g
Sodium: 1026mg
Fiber: 3 g
Protein: 4 g
Carbohydrates: 12 g
Sugars: 7 g

Chicken Nibbles

Preparation Time: 2 hours 10 minutes
Cooking Time: 5 minutes
Servings: 6
Ingredients:

- ½ cup water
- 1 teaspoon sugar
- ½ teaspoon ginger
- Vegetable oil as needed
- 1 ½ cups breadcrumbs
- ¼ teaspoon garlic powder
- ¾ cup low-sodium soy sauce
- 1 pound boneless & skinless chicken breast

Directions:

1. Stir soy sauce, garlic powder, water, and ginger together in a bowl.
2. Cut the chicken into 2 x 1 x 112-inch pieces.
3. Rub the chicken with the mix and let it stay for two hours.
4. Drain and roll the pieces in the breadcrumbs.
5. Deep fat fry the chicken in vegetable oil at 375 degrees Fahrenheit (190°C) for a minute.
6. Put on absorbent towels to trap excess oil, and serve once done!

Nutrition:
Calories: 193
Fat: 2 g
Sodium: 312mg
Fiber: 1 g
Protein: 21 g
Carbohydrates: 12 g
Sugars: 2

Sherry Chicken Liver

Preparation Time: 10 minutes
Cooking Time: 20 minutes
Servings: 10

Ingredients:

- 2 oz. milk
- 2 oz. sherry
- 1 minced garlic clove
- 10 oz. chicken livers
- ⅛ teaspoon nutmeg
- 4 tablespoons olive oil
- 4 slices low-sodium bacon
- ½ cup finely chopped onion
- 4 tablespoons fresh rosemary

Directions:

1. Heat the oil in a large sauté pan over low heat and cook onion and bacon for 4 minutes.
2. Add in garlic and liver to cook for 15 minutes on medium heat.
3. Mix rosemary and sherry and simmer on low heat for 15 minutes or until the liver is cooked through.
4. Sprinkle a pinch of pepper and nutmeg.
5. Remove the pan from the heat and set aside to cool.
6. Add the cooled liver mix to the food processor and puree until smooth.
7. Mix in the milk gradually and pulse until blended.
8. Spread the blend on whole wheat bread or bun and serve!

Nutrition:

Calories: 128
Fat: 9 g
Sodium: 212mg
Fiber: 1 g
Protein: 8 g
Carbohydrates: 2 g

CHAPTER 9:
SMOOTHIES & BEVERAGES

Healthy Green Smoothie

Preparation Time: 5 minutes
Cooking Time: 0 minutes
Servings: 1
Ingredients:
- 1 large ripe banana
- ¼ ripe avocado
- 1 cup unsweetened almond milk
- 1 cup packed baby kale
- 1 cup ice cubes
- 2 tablespoons honey
- 1 tablespoon chia seeds

Directions:
1. Add all the ingredients in a blender and leave the ice cubes.
2. Blend until the smoothie becomes smooth and creamy on a high setting.
3. Add ice cubes and blend again until smooth.
4. Pour into a glass and serve immediately.

Nutrition:
Calories: 383
Fat: 14 g
Sodium: 199mg
Fiber: 0 g
Protein: 6 g
Carbohydrates: 55 g
Sugars: 12 g

Mango Kale Smoothie

Preparation Time: 10 minutes
Cooking Time: 0 minutes
Servings: 1
Ingredients:
- 1 sliced small banana
- 1 cup baby kale
- 1 cup frozen mango chunks
- 1 cup fresh orange juice

Directions:
1. Put all the ingredients in the blender and blend on a medium-low setting.
2. Once the ingredients are well combined, set the speed to medium-high until the consistency turns smooth.
3. Pour the smoothie into a glass and serve immediately.

Nutrition:
Calories: 329
Fat: 1 g
Sodium: 10mg
Fiber: 6 g
Protein: 4 g
Carbohydrates: 82 g
Sugars: 62 g

Pineapple Smoothie

Preparation Time: 10 minutes
Cooking Time: 10 minutes
Servings: 1

Ingredients:
- 1 cup frozen pineapple chunks
- 1 cup baby kale
- ½ cup unsweetened coconut milk
- ½ fresh orange juice
- ¼ cup low-fat plain or coconut-flavored Greek yogurt

Directions:
1. Put all the ingredients in the blender.
2. Blend on medium-low speed setting until well combined.
3. Increase the setting to medium-high until completely smooth.
4. Pour the smoothie into a glass and serve immediately.

Nutrition:
Calories: 213
Fat: 3 g
Sodium: 28mg
Fiber: 4 g
Protein: 9 g
Carbohydrates: 41 g
Sugars: 17 g

Strawberry & Tofu Smoothie

Preparation Time: 10 minutes
Cooking Time: 10 minutes
Servings: 2

Ingredients:
- 10 frozen strawberries
- 1 cup almond milk
- ½ cup silken tofu
- 2 tablespoons sugar

Directions:
1. Put all the ingredients in the blender.
2. Blend on medium-high speed setting for 1 minute until smooth and frothy.
3. Pour the smoothie into a glass and serve immediately.

Nutrition:
Calories: 171
Fat: 3 g
Sodium: 105mg
Fiber: 2 g
Protein: 5 g
Carbohydrates: 30 g
Sugars: 24 g

Immunity Tea

Preparation Time: 10 minutes
Cooking Time: 20 minutes
Servings: 1
Ingredients:
- 1 part rosehip
- 1 part echinacea
- 1 part astragalus
- 1 part chamomile
- 1 part elderflowers
- 1 part elderberries

Directions:
1. Combine all the ingredients and store them in an airtight jar.
2. Use only when making tea; add one teaspoon into a tea ball or bag and add it to 8 ounces of water.
3. Let it steep for 20 minutes before serving!

Nutrition:
Calories: 0
Fat: 0 g
Sodium: 0mg
Fiber: 0 g
Protein: 0 g
Carbohydrates: 1 g
Sugars: 0 g

Lemongrass Tea

Preparation Time: 5 minutes
Cooking Time: 15 minutes
Servings: 3
Ingredients:
- Agave syrup as needed
- 5 teaspoons dried lemongrass
- 5 teaspoons dried lemon thyme
- 1 teaspoon dried lemon verbena

Directions:
1. Boil water in a pot and add the dried herbs.
2. Mix, cover, and let it steep for 15 minutes.
3. Strain well and serve it with some agave syrup if you prefer tea sweet.

Nutrition:
Calories: 0
Fat: 0 g
Sodium: 0mg
Fiber: 0 g
Protein: 0 g
Carbohydrates: 0 g
Sugars: 0 g

Berry Spinach Smoothie

Preparation Time: 15 minutes
Cooking Time: 0 minutes
Serves: 8

Ingredients:

- 1 cup fresh blackberries
- 1 cup pomegranate juice
- 1 cup fresh baby spinach leaves
- 1 cup frozen unsweetened raspberries
- 2 cups frozen unsweetened strawberries
- 3 tablespoons sugar-free vanilla-flavor protein powder

Directions:

1. Blend all the ingredients in a high-speed blender until creamy.
2. Pour into glasses to serve!

Nutrition:

Calories: 307
Fat: 3 g
Sodium: 200mg
Fiber: 11 g
Protein: 28 g
Carbohydrates: 30 g
Sugars: 5 g

Sweet Potato Smoothie

Preparation Time: 5 minutes
Cooking Time: 10 minutes
Servings: 1

Ingredients:

- ¼ cup nutmeg
- ½ frozen banana
- ½ teaspoon sea salt
- 1 tablespoon almond butter
- ½ cup frozen zucchini pieces
- 1 scoop vanilla protein powder
- 1 ½ cups unsweetened almond milk
- 1 cup cooked and cubed frozen sweet potato

Directions:

1. Add all the ingredients mentioned above to the blender.
2. Blend the ingredients on high speed for 2-3 minutes or until everything's smooth.
3. Pour the smoothie into a glass and enjoy!

Nutrition:

Calories: 235
Fat: 9 g
Sodium: 137mg
Fiber: 7 g
Protein: 14 g
Carbohydrates: 24 g
Sugars: 0 g

Berry & Banana Smoothie

Preparation Time: 10 minutes
Cooking Time: 2 minutes
Servings: 5

Ingredients:

- 2 ½ cups sliced banana
- 2 ½ cups whole berries of choice
- 5 cups unsweetened vanilla almond milk/soy milk

Directions:

1. Add ½ cup berries and ½ cup banana in a plastic seal bag.
2. Follow the same process with the remaining fruit.
3. Keep refrigerated until use, and use only one bag when you need to.
4. Add the contents of one bag in the blender with milk and blend until smooth.
5. Pour into a glass and serve!

Nutrition:

Calories: 125
Fat: 2 g
Sodium: 0mg
Fiber: 6 g
Protein: 6 g
Carbohydrates: 23 g
Sugars: 31 g

Orange Berry Smoothie

Preparation Time: 15 minutes
Cooking Time: 0 minutes
Servings: 4

Ingredients:

- 1 banana
- 1 tablespoon sugar
- ½ cup low-fat plain yogurt
- 1 ¼ cups any frozen berries
- 1 ¼ cups calcium-fortified orange juice

Directions:

1. Blend all the ingredients in a high-speed blender until creamy.
2. Pour into glasses to serve!

Nutrition:

Calories: 405
Fat: 7 g
Sodium: 40mg
Fiber: 2 g
Protein: 8 g
Carbohydrates: 85 g
Sugars: 2 g

Sweet Protein Shake

Preparation Time: 5 minutes
Cooking Time: 0 minutes
Servings: 1

Ingredients:
- ½ cup ice
- A pinch of Kosher salt
- ¾ cup almond milk
- 1 tablespoon chia seeds
- 2 tablespoons hemp seeds
- 3 tablespoons sugar/stevia
- 2 tablespoons almond butter
- ½ tablespoon pure vanilla extract
- 2 tablespoons unsweetened cocoa powder

Directions:
1. Blend all the ingredients in a blender until smooth.
2. Pour in glasses to serve, and enjoy!

Nutrition:
Calories: 171
Fat: 8 g
Sodium: 212mg
Fiber: 10 g
Protein: 19 g
Carbohydrates: 2 g
Sugars: 1 g

Spinach Grapefruit Smoothie

Preparation Time: 8 minutes
Cooking Time: 2 minutes
Servings: 6

Ingredients:
- 1 cup ice
- 1 cup plain coconut water
- 1 cup packed baby spinach
- 1 cup frozen diced pineapple
- ½ teaspoon grated fresh ginger
- 1 peeled & segmented with extra juice saved small grapefruit

Directions:
1. Blend all the ingredients in the blender until smooth and frothy.
2. Pour into glasses and serve!

Nutrition:
Calories: 127
Fat: 0 g
Sodium: 25mg
Fiber: 5 g
Protein: 2 g
Carbohydrates: 32 g
Sugars: 21 g

Almond Cherry Smoothie

Preparation Time: 4 minutes
Cooking Time: 20 minutes
Servings: 3

Ingredients:

- ½ cup oat milk
- 1 teaspoon cocoa powder
- 1 tablespoon brown sugar
- ½ teaspoon vanilla extract
- 1 tablespoon almond butter
- 1 cup frozen dark sweet cherries

Direction:

1. Blend all the ingredients in the blender until smooth.
2. Pour into glasses and serve!

Nutrition:

Calories: 326
Fat:10 g
Sodium: 25mg
Fiber: 11 g
Protein: 7 g
Carbohydrates: 56 g
Sugars: 32 g

Honey Green Tea Smoothie

Preparation Time: 4 minutes
Cooking Time: 2 minutes
Servings: 3

Ingredients:

- 1 tablespoon honey
- 1 tablespoon lemon juice
- 1 cup cold unsweetened green tea
- 2 cups frozen unsweetened mixed fruit

Directions:

1. Blend all the ingredients in the blender until smooth and frothy.
2. Pour into glasses and serve!

Nutrition:

Calories: 106
Fat:0 g
Sodium: 3mg
Fiber: 11 g
Protein: 1 g
Carbohydrates: 27 g
Sugars: 9 g

Pumpkin Coconut Smoothie

Preparation Time: 15 minutes

Cooking Time: 0 minutes

Servings: 2

Ingredients:

- 1 cup ice
- 1 cup coconut milk
- 1 frozen sliced banana
- ¼ cup organic pumpkin puree
- 2 teaspoons pumpkin pie spice/ginger/cinnamon

Directions:

1. Blend all the ingredients in a blender until smooth.
2. Pour in glasses to serve, and enjoy!

Nutrition:

Calories: 292

Fat:24 g

Sodium: 18mg

Fiber: 2 g

Protein: 3 g

Carbohydrates: 20 g

Sugars: 8 g

Chapter 10:
Sugar-Free Desserts

Berry & Mango Frozen Yogurt

Preparation Time: 5 minutes

Cooking Time: 0 minutes

Servings: 5

Ingredients:

- 1½ cups any fresh/frozen berries
- 1 sweet peeled & chopped ripe/frozen mango
- ¾ cup sweetened/flavored plain yogurt
- 2 cups chopped fresh seasonal fruit

Directions:

1. Take a tray or line a dish with baking paper and put berries and chopped mango if you're using fresh fruits.
2. Put them in the freezer till they become hard.
3. Take them out to thaw for 10 minutes before adding them to a food processor.
4. Add in yogurt and blend until smooth.
5. Take the contents out in bowls using a spatula.
6. Serve immediately with fresh fruit or freeze for something before serving.

Nutrition:

Calories:148

Fat: 0 g

Sodium: 18mg

Fiber: 5 g

Protein: 6 g

Carbohydrates: 26 g

Sugars: 24 g

Mango & Passionfruit Ice Cream

Preparation Time:15 minutes

Cooking Time: 0 minutes

Servings: 8

Ingredients:

- 3 large, chopped bananas
- 12 oz. frozen diced mango
- 1 cup unsweetened coconut milk
- 2 large passionfruit pulp and extra to serve
- Diced fresh mango

Directions:

1. Put the banana on a tray in a single layer and freeze for three hours.
2. Thaw the banana and mango for some time before adding to the blender and process until mixed well.
3. Next, pour in the milk and process it, scraping it down from the sides after some time.
4. Blend until the mixture reaches a sorbet-like consistency.
5. Take out the mixture into a loaf pan or airtight container with a spoon.
6. Layer the passionfruit pulp on top, cover, and let it freeze overnight.
7. Garnish it with extra pulp and fresh mango before serving.

Nutrition:

Calories: 99

Fat: 1 g

Sodium: 20mg

Fiber: 2 g

Protein: 1 g

Carbohydrates: 18 g

Sugars: 12 g

Pistachio & Date Bites

Preparation Time: 10 minutes
Cooking Time: 0 minutes
Servings: 32
Ingredients:
- 2 cups pitted whole dates
- 1 cup golden raisins
- 1 cup salt-free & shelled raw pistachios
- 1 teaspoon ground fennel seeds
- ¼ teaspoon ground pepper

Directions:
1. Add all the ingredients in the food processor and process until finely chopped.
2. Create 32 small balls (a tablespoon each) out of the mixture.
3. You can store them at room temperature in an airtight container for up to 3 hours or refrigerate them for snacking.

Nutrition:
Calories: 68
Fat: 2 g
Sodium: 1mg
Fiber: 1 g
Protein: 1 g
Carbohydrates: 13 g
Sugars: 11 g

Chocolate Banana Bites

Preparation Time: 2 hours 30 minutes
Cooking Time: 0 minutes
Servings: 24
Ingredients:
- 3 large bananas
- ¾ cup vegan chocolate chips
- ¼ cup natural peanut butter

Directions:
1. Peel the bananas and slice each in half lengthwise.
2. Spread peanut butter on each half and close them together to create a banana sandwich.
3. Now slice the right rounds or circles from each banana.
4. Line a tray or baking sheet with parchment or butter paper.
5. Arrange the banana bites on the prepared tray and freeze them overnight or for two hours.
6. Meanwhile, add chocolate chips to a microwave-safe bowl and heat them for one and a half minutes in 15-second increments on high until melted.
7. Take each frozen banana slice and dip half in the chocolate.
8. Let it stand until the chocolate is firm.
9. Or you can serve it immediately or freeze it for a few minutes to set the chocolate before serving.

Nutrition (Per Serving):
Calories: 58
Fat: 3 g
Sodium: 10mg
Fiber: 1 g
Protein: 1 g
Carbohydrates: 8 g
Sugars: 5 g

Date & Mango Energy Bites

Preparation Time: 15 minutes
Cooking Time: 0 minutes
Servings: 20

Ingredients:

- 2 cups pitted whole dates
- 1 cup dried mango/another dried fruit
- 1 cup raw cashews
- ¼ teaspoon salt

Directions:

1. Add all the ingredients in the food processor and process until finely chopped.
2. Create 20 balls (two tablespoons each) out of the mixture.
3. You can store them at room temperature in an airtight container or refrigerate them for snacking for more than a week.

Nutrition:

Calories: 73
Fat: 3 g
Sodium: 35mg
Fiber: 1 g
Protein: 1 g
Carbohydrates: 11 g
Sugars: 9 g

Peach & Pistachio Toast

Preparation Time: 5 minutes
Cooking Time: 0 minutes
Servings: 1

Ingredients:

- ½ medium sliced peach
- 1 whole wheat toasted bread slice
- 1 tablespoon low-fat ricotta cheese
- 1 tablespoon chopped pistachios
- 1 teaspoon honey, divided
- ⅛ teaspoon cinnamon

Directions:

1. Add cinnamon, ricotta, and ½ teaspoon honey in a bowl.
2. Combine the mixture and spread on the toasted bread slice.
3. Top with peach, sprinkle pistachios, and drizzle the remaining ½ teaspoon honey to serve immediately.

Nutrition:

Calories: 193
Fat: 6 g
Sodium: 157mg
Fiber: 4 g
Protein: 8 g
Carbohydrates: 29 g
Sugars: 9 g

Pineapple Ice Cream

Preparation Time: 5 minutes
Cooking Time: 0 minutes
Servings: 6

Ingredients:

- 16 oz. package of frozen pineapple chunks
- 1 cup frozen mango chunks
- 1 tablespoon lemon juice

Directions:

1. Add all the ingredients in the food processor and process until smooth and creamy.
2. In case of frozen ingredients, add ¼ water to the mix if needed for the desired consistency.
3. Serve immediately for the best texture and experience.

Nutrition:

Calories: 55
Fat: 0 g
Sodium: 1mg
Fiber: 2 g
Protein: 1 g
Carbohydrates: 14 g
Sugars: 11 g

Melon Pops

Preparation Time: 5 minutes
Cooking Time: 0 minutes
Servings: 6

Ingredients:

- 2 tablespoons lime juice
- 3 cups 1-inch cubed & seedless watermelon, cantaloupe, & honeydew melon

Directions:

1. Add all the ingredients in the food processor and pulse until smooth.
2. Fill six freezer pop molds with the blend and place them in the freezer.
3. Freeze for one hour and a half or until set.
4. You can keep them frozen for over a week.
5. Serve when you prefer and enjoy.

Nutrition:

Calories: 28
Fat: 0 g
Sodium: 1mg
Fiber: 0 g
Protein: 1 g
Carbohydrates: 16 g
Sugars: 2 g

Watermelon Sherbet

Preparation Time: 8 hours 10 minutes
Cooking Time: 0 minutes
Servings: 12

Ingredients:

- 14 oz. can sweetened condensed milk
- 6 ¼ cups cubed & seedless watermelon
- ⅓ cup lime juice
- ¼ teaspoon salt

Directions:

1. Take a large, rimmed baking sheet and place the watermelon on it.
2. Freeze it for 4 hours or overnight until frozen.
3. Add all the ingredients, including the frozen watermelon cubes, to the food processor.
4. Work in batches if you must, and puree the mixture for 2-3 minutes until smooth.
5. Transfer the puree to a large sealable container, cover it, and freeze it for 4 hours or overnight until set.
6. Serve immediately and enjoy!

Nutrition:

Calories: 132
Fat: 3 g
Sodium: 91mg
Fiber: 0 g
Protein: 3 g
Carbohydrates: 25 g
Sugars: 23 g

Apple Fruit Salad

Preparation Time: 7 hours 10 minutes
Cooking Time: 0 minutes
Servings: 6

Ingredients:

- 1 thinly sliced stalk celery
- 2 tablespoons dried currants
- ½ cup plain low-fat Greek yogurt
- ¼ cup toasted & chopped walnuts
- ½ cup halved red seedless grapes
- 2 Granny Smith apples, halved, cored, & cut into ¾-inch pieces
- 2 barely ripe Bartlett pears, halved, cored, and cut into ¾-inch pieces

Directions:

1. Mix all the ingredients together except yogurt.
2. Add in the yogurt and carefully toss to combine.
3. Chill for up to 6 hours before serving, or serve as it is with walnuts sprinkled on top.

Nutrition:

Calories: 115
Fat: 3 g
Sodium: 10mg
Fiber: 0 g
Protein: 3 g
Carbohydrates: 22 g
Sugars: 4 g

Yogurt Berry Parfaits

Preparation Time: 10 minutes
Cooking Time: 0 minutes
Servings: 4

Ingredients:

- 1 cup fresh raspberries
- 1 cup fresh blueberries
- 1 cup plain fat-free yogurt
- 2 cups halved fresh strawberries

Directions:

1. Lightly mash raspberries with a fork or a masher in a bowl.
2. Stir in yogurt and combine thoroughly.
3. Layer half yogurt mix, half strawberries, and ¼ cup blueberries into 4 parfait glasses or bowls.
4. Chill before serving or at once.

Nutrition:

Calories: 94
Fat: 3 g
Sodium: 89mg
Fiber: 5 g
Protein: 5 g
Carbohydrates: 19 g
Sugars: 1 g

Roasted Pears with Yogurt

Preparation Time: 10 minutes
Cooking Time: 0 minutes
Servings: 4

Ingredients:

- 4 teaspoons honey
- 3 teaspoons canola oil divided
- ⅛ teaspoon ground cinnamon
- 1⅓ cups plain low-fat Greek yogurt
- 2 tablespoons toasted & chopped walnuts
- 2 medium pears, each cut into 8 wedges

Directions:

1. Start by preheating the oven to 400 degrees Fahrenheit.
2. Brush 2 teaspoons oil on large, rimmed baking sheets
3. Add the pears in a bowl and drizzle the remaining teaspoon oil on top.
4. Sprinkle cinnamon and toss to coat the pears.
5. Place the pears cut side down on the prepared baking sheet in a single layer.
6. Roast, flipping once, for 25-30 minutes or until it's lightly browned and soft.
7. Take out and allow to cool for a few minutes.
8. Serve ⅓ cup yogurt equally in 4 bowls and divide pears equally around the yogurt.
9. Drizzle honey and walnuts on top before serving.

Nutrition:

Calories: 171
Fat: 7 g
Sodium: 89mg
Fiber: 5 g
Protein: 7 g
Carbohydrates: 22 g
Sugars: 2 g

Shortbread Cookies

Preparation Time: 10 minutes
Cooking Time: 20 minutes
Servings: 6

Ingredients:

- ½ cup erythritol
- 2 ½ cups almond flour
- 6 tablespoons low-fat butter
- 1 teaspoon vanilla essence

Directions:

1. Line the cookie sheet with parchment paper and preheat the oven to 350 degrees Fahrenheit.
2. Whisk butter and erythritol until fluffy and mix in vanilla essence and almond flour.
3. Mix well until crumbly, and use a tablespoon to scoop out cookie dough onto the prepared sheet.
4. Bake for 15 minutes or until golden brown.
5. Serve immediately with tea!

Nutrition:

Calories: 145
Fat: 7 g
Sodium: 0mg
Fiber: 7 g
Protein: 1 g
Carbohydrates: 18 g
Sugars: 3 g

Banana Greek Yogurt Bowl

Preparation Time: 5 minutes
Cooking Time: 0 minutes
Servings: 4

Ingredients:

- 1 teaspoon nutmeg
- ¼ cup flaxseed meal
- 4 cups vanilla Greek yogurt
- 2 medium peeled & sliced bananas
- ¼ cup creamy natural peanut butter

Directions:

1. Divide yogurt into four serving bowls.
2. Melt peanut butter in a microwave-safe bowl in the microwave for 40 seconds.
3. Add one tablespoon of peanut butter to all yogurt bowls and top with banana slices.
4. Serve with nutmeg and flaxseed on top, and enjoy!

Nutrition:

Calories: 370
Fat: 11 g
Sodium: 146mg
Fiber: 4 g
Protein: 22 g
Carbohydrates: 47 g
Sugars: 34 g

Vanilla Rice Pudding

Preparation Time: 10 minutes
Cooking Time: 1 hour 35 minutes
Servings: 6

Ingredients:

- ¼ teaspoon nutmeg
- ½ teaspoon cinnamon
- ½ teaspoon fine sea salt
- 3 tablespoons applesauce
- 3 cups light coconut milk
- 2 cups cooked brown rice
- 1 teaspoon pure vanilla extract

Directions:

1. Pour all the ingredients into a two-quart dish after blending them all together.
2. Bake at 300 degrees Fahrenheit for 90 minutes.
3. Serve once when it is cooled.

Nutrition:

Calories: 330
Fat: 6 g
Sodium: 350mg
Fiber: 0 g
Protein: 9 g
Carbohydrates: 60 g
Sugars: 37 g

60-DAY MEAL PLAN

Week 1

Breakfast	Lunch	Dinner	Dessert
Yummy Jelly & Peanut Butter Oatmeal	Healthy Chickpea Bowl	Vegan Spinach Ricotta	Banana Greek Yogurt Bowl
Gluten-Free Banana Oat Muffins	Avocado Chicken Wraps	Parsley Lemon Pasta	Vanilla Rice Pudding
Breakfast Chia Seeds Chocolate Pudding	Zucchini Hummus	Quick Peas Mash	Sweet Protein Shake
Sweet Potato Smoothie	Red Bean Salad	Chickpea Turmeric Stew	Spinach Grapefruit Smoothie
Berry & Banana Smoothie	Turkey Vegetable Sauté	Grilled Chicken Breasts	Quinoa Apple Salad
Orange Berry Smoothie	Borscht	Grilled Chicken Thighs	Arugula Fruit Salad
Orange Berry Smoothie (leftovers)	Chicken Nibbles	Lemon & Butter Salmon	Gluten-Free Banana Oat Muffins

Week 2

Breakfast	Lunch	Dinner	Dessert
Nutritional Tofu Scramble	Cucumber and Chickpea Bowl	Sherry Chicken Liver	Almond Cherry Smoothie
Delicious Quinoa & Apple Breakfast Porridge	Chicken Avocado Cups	Flavored Octopus	Honey Green Tea Smoothie
Simple Avocado Toast	Spinach Chips	Fish Stew	Roasted Pears with Yogurt
Nut Cream Cheese & Strawberry Sandwich	Artichoke Salad	Baked Chicken Breast	Shortbread Cookies
Overnight Cinnamon Oats	Soy Pasta Soup	Herb Turkey Roast	Ambrosia Fruit Salad
Mango & Pomegranate Breakfast Smoothie	Ginger Chicken	Italian Bean Chicken	Nut Cream Cheese & Strawberry Sandwich
Breakfast Fruity Quinoa Mix	Orange Baked Chicken	Vegetables & Lentil Stew	Arugula Fruit Salad

Week 3

Breakfast	Lunch	Dinner	Dessert
Quick Breakfast Tacos	Salmon & Bean Salad Broccoli	Creamy Mushroom Stroganoff	Mango Kale Smoothie
Sweet Potatoes with A Twist	Avocado Salsa	Tomato Basil Pasta	Pineapple Smoothie
Gluten-Free Blueberry Pancakes	Fulfilling Beans Mix	Mushroom Turkey Meatballs	Strawberry & Tofu Smoothie
Crunchy Almond Cereal Breakfast	Healthy Kale Bowls	Herb White Beans Stew	Watermelon Sherbet
Banana Cocoa Smoothie	Healthy Veggie Sticks	One Pot Chickpea Curry	Apple Fruit Salad
Quick Breakfast Tacos	Mediterranean Lunch	Salmon & Kale	Yogurt Berry Parfaits
Sweet Potatoes with A Twist	Italian Mushroom Soup	Salmon & Kalamata Olives	Quinoa Apple Salad

Week 4

Breakfast	Lunch	Dinner	Dessert
Almond Cherry Smoothie	Healthy Carrot Soup	Chicken Mushrooms Stroganoff	Peach & Pistachio Toast
Honey Green Tea Smoothie	Gluten-Free Stuffed Potatoes	Latin Chicken	Pineapple Ice Cream
Pumpkin Coconut Smoothie	Celery & Arugula Salad	Creamy Lemon Garlic Pasta	Melon Pops
Delicious Quinoa & Apple Breakfast Porridge	Cucumber Jicama Salad	Cajun Crab	Pumpkin Coconut Smoothie
Simple Avocado Toast	Roasted Root Vegetables	Greek Chicken Drumettes	Gluten-Free Banana Oat Muffins
Nut Cream Cheese & Strawberry Sandwich	Roasted Mint Carrots	Chicken Mushrooms Stroganoff	Banana Cocoa Smoothie
Overnight Cinnamon Oats	Sesame Chicken Wings	Latin Chicken	Vanilla Rice Pudding

Week 5

Breakfast	Lunch	Dinner	Dessert
Overnight Cinnamon Oats	Green Bean Fries	Herb Crust Grilled Salmon	Berry & Mango Frozen Yogurt
Mango & Pomegranate Breakfast Smoothie	Yummy Lentil Cakes	Grilled Black Cod	Mango & Passionfruit Ice Cream
Breakfast Fruity Quinoa Mix	Chicken & Cabbage Stir-Fry	Cajun Crab	Pistachio & Date Bites
Quick Breakfast Tacos	Turkey & Swiss Sandwich	Arugula Pesto Pasta	Lemongrass Tea
Sweet Potatoes with A Twist	Gnocchi With Zucchini Ribbons	Vegetable Orzo Pasta	Berry Spinach Smoothie
Gluten-Free Blueberry Pancakes	Thai-Style Eggplant Dip	Crumbly Spaghetti Fritters	Sweet Potato Smoothie
Crunchy Almond Cereal Breakfast	Greek Avocado Salad	Vegetables & Lentil Stew	Walnut & Berry Salad

Week 6

Breakfast	Lunch	Dinner	Dessert
Gluten-Free Banana Oat Muffins	Greek Chicken Salad	Cheese & Beet Fettuccine Pasta	Quinoa Apple Salad
Breakfast Chia Seeds Chocolate Pudding	Easy Broccoli Salad	Creamy Brussels Sprouts Fettuccine	Arugula Fruit Salad
Nutritional Tofu Scramble	Potato Barley Soup	Kale Pesto Noodles	Chocolate Banana Bites
Delicious Quinoa & Apple Breakfast Porridge	Air Fried Onion Rings	Chicken Jambalaya	Date & Mango Energy Bites
Simple Avocado Toast	Healthy Potato Casserole	Tuna Patties	Yogurt Berry Parfaits
Nut Cream Cheese & Strawberry Sandwich	Parmesan Roasted Broccoli	Fish Chowder	Roasted Pears with Yogurt
Overnight Cinnamon Oats	Vegetable Minestrone	Broiled Fish Fillets	Shortbread Cookies

Week 7

Breakfast	Lunch	Dinner	Dessert
Spinach Frittata	Berry Avocado salad	Orange Baked Chicken	Healthy Green Smoothie
Potatoes & Egg Scramble	Cherry Tuna Salad	Turkey Vegetable Sauté	Mango Kale Smoothie
Simple Air Fried Pancake	Easy Quinoa Bowl	Ginger Congee	Pineapple Smoothie
Quick Ricotta Fig Toast	Ginger Congee	Healthy Potato Casserole	Strawberry & Tofu Smoothie
Tasty Vegetable Frittata	Tasty Chicken Sticks	Baked Chicken Breast	Pineapple Ice Cream
Quick Chicken Strips	Chicken Skewers	Herb Turkey Roast	Melon Pops
Chicken Hash For Breakfast	Black-Eyed Peas Dip	Mushroom Turkey Meatballs	Watermelon Sherbet

Week 8

Breakfast	Lunch	Dinner	Dessert
Yummy Jelly & Peanut Butter Oatmeal	Chipotle Kidney Beans Burrito Bowl	Macaroni With Low-Fat Cheese	Apple Fruit Salad
Gluten-Free Banana Oat Muffins	Sweet Potato & Black Bean Chilli	Tuna Mushroom Noodles	Yogurt Berry Parfaits
Breakfast Chia Seeds Chocolate Pudding	Vegetable Minestrone	Chipotle Kidney Beans Burrito Bowl	Roasted Pears with Yogurt
Sweet Potato Smoothie	Vegan Brown Rice Burgers	Sweet Potato & Black Bean Chilli	Shortbread Cookies
Berry & Banana Smoothie	Walnut & Berry Salad	Burrata Pasta With Cherry Tomatoes	Banana Greek Yogurt Bowl
Orange Berry Smoothie	Spinach & Orange Salad	Cornmeal Fish Fillets	Vanilla Rice Pudding
Orange Berry Smoothie (leftovers)	Tomato Macaroni	Peppered Mackerel Fillets	Sweet Protein Shake

Made in the USA
Las Vegas, NV
17 April 2024

88811658R00063